PATRICK MOORE AND DAVID A. HARDY

D1612069

CHALLENGE OF THE STARS

Foreword by Arthur C. Clarke

Epilogue by Dr James C. Fletcher NASA

Mitchell Beazley Limited London

In association with
Sidgwick & Jackson Limited

CONTENTS

Mitchell Beazley Limited
14–15 Manette Street, London W1
First published 1972

Challenge of the Stars © Mitchell Beazley Limited 1972
48 original illustrations by David A. Hardy © David A. Hardy 1972
All other illustrations and text © Mitchell Beazley Limited 1972

Distributed by George Philip & Son Limited
12–14 Floral Street, London WC2
Filmset by Oliver Burridge Filmsetting Limited,
Crawley, Sussex, England.
Printed and bound in Great Britain by
Sir Joseph Causton and Sons Limited,
Eastleigh, Hampshire, England
ISBN 0 85533 007 4

The 'ring of fire' *frontispiece*
The most essential requirement for the inhabitants of the planet Earth, for it encompasses all life on our world. It is our atmosphere, which refracts sunlight during an eclipse of the Sun, seen from a vantage point some thirty miles above the surface of the Moon.

FOREWORD

Everyone knows the rôle that science-fiction writers have played in presenting the idea of space travel to the world decades – indeed, centuries – before it was actually achieved. It might well be argued that if there had been no writers, there would be no astronauts today. Before the reality, there must be the dream to provide inspiration.

The rôle of the space artists, however, has been much less appreciated, perhaps because there are so few of them; the good ones can be counted on the fingers. I do not know who first tried to visualize the Earth as a planet; it could well have been the ubiquitous Leonardo, whose notebooks contain some remarkable 'aerial' views of cities and landscapes. It would seem unlike him, not to have taken these to their logical conclusion.

Popular books on astronomy, over the last few centuries, must occasionally have regaled their readers with space-views of the Earth and Moon. Perhaps the most outstanding example is Nasmyth and Carpenter's classic *The Moon* (1874) which employed a combination of plaster models and photography to give strikingly realistic views of lunar landscapes. However, it was the rise of the science-fiction magazines in the 1930s that first gave the space-artist a popular audience; scanning back through my memories, the very first science-fiction magazine I ever saw was a *circa* 1929 issue of *Amazing Stories*, with a cover showing Jupiter hanging above the landscape of one of its satellites. The artist was Frank R. Paul – whose exotic space-vistas, bug-eyed extraterrestrials, and apparently cloned humans will be remembered with affection by all old-timers.

It must be admitted that most of the pulp-magazine artists – who had little knowledge of science, and were probably even more miserably paid than the writers – were concerned with entertainment rather than with accuracy. That both could be combined was demonstrated when *Life* Magazine, in the early 1940s, published Chesley Bonestell's stunning views of Saturn from Titan, Mimas and its other moons. I can still recall the impact of those paintings – and my annoyance because some earth-bound *Life* editor had remarked of the tiny figures in Chesley's moonscapes that they were merely put in 'to give scale'. To give scale, indeed! Didn't he have the imagination to realize that some day men would actually *be* out there, looking up at the ringed glory of the most spectacular of all the planets?

Though it will be some little while yet before human explorers reach Saturn, we are now in an interesting transition period when we can compare the realities of space with the earlier imaginings of the artists. The Gemini photos of Earth, the Orbiter and Apollo photos of the Moon – these have largely confirmed, but have not superseded, the creations of the astro-painters. The camera (despite many nineteenth century fears) failed to displace the easel on *this* planet; nor will it do so in space. In fact, we have already had one orbiting painter (Cosmonaut Alexei Leonov), and there will be many others in the years to come.

But the astronomical artist, like the writer, will always be far ahead of the explorer. He can depict scenes which no human eye will ever witness, because of their danger, or their remoteness in time or space. Only through the eye of imagination can we watch the formation of the planets, the explosion of a super-nova, the ball-bearing smooth surface of a neutron star, or the view of our own Galaxy, looking back from its off-shore islands, the Clouds of Magellan.

Of course, the space-artist can sometimes be proven wrong – but that is part of the fun. Pre-Apollo moonscapes were invariably too jagged, and few if any artists (or scientists) anticipated the softly-yielding soil of the *maria*. Nor did anyone expect Mars to be covered with craters that would have looked perfectly at home on the Moon; or a Venus that rotated backwards and was almost red-hot; or a Mercury that had sunrise and sunset. There will be other surprises to come.

I welcome this book by David Hardy and my old friend Patrick Moore, because it provides a heady mixture of education, entertainment – and inspiration. We need the latter, now that the excitement of the Apollo programme has ebbed, and so many voices are asking 'Why go to the planets?' David Hardy's poetically luminous paintings are a reminder that the Moon is not the goal, but merely the beginning, of *real* space exploration.

This book also gives me a reassuring feeling of progress – of the continuity of human effort. It is now almost twenty years since I was working, with the late R. A. Smith, on the text and illustrations of *The Exploration of the Moon*, a forecast of the early days of manned spaceflight. That book has long been out of print, because most of it is now past history; but it is sometimes fun to glance back over its pages.

In the same way, I look forward to checking the accuracy of David Hardy's visions – twenty years from now.

Arthur C. Clarke
New York
January 1972

INTRODUCTION

The twentieth century has been the Age of Challenge. In its earliest years, Man took to the air; since then he has explored the ocean bed, and has reached the summits of our highest mountains. In the last decade, he has done more. He has reached the Moon, and has sent his messengers out to other planets. We have lived through the beginning of the greatest challenge of all: the invasion of outer space.

Much has been achieved already, and critics of the space programme conveniently forget the immense practical benefits which have become apparent. Communications satellites have become part of our everyday life; many lives have been saved by the weather satellites, which have given advance warnings of dangerous tropical storms; all branches of science have shared in the profits. Yet this is only a beginning. In this book we are looking to the future – to the time when we reach not only the planets, but also the stars. It is a breathtaking prospect.

The idea of space-travel is not new. Indeed, it goes back to at least the second century A.D., when a Greek satirist, Lucian, wrote a story about a voyage to the Moon. Other writers followed in Lucian's footsteps, but it was not until our own time that space-travel became a practical possibility. Konstantin Tsiolkovskii, a shy, deaf Russian teacher, wrote about it in scientific vein just about the time that the Wright Brothers were making their first 'hops' from Kitty Hawk; and yet after the First World War Robert Goddard, the American who fired the first liquid-propellant rocket in history, was ridiculed for daring to suggest that small vehicles might be sent as far as the Moon.

At that time, of course, rockets were both feeble and unreliable. There seemed no other method of reaching space; the atmosphere of the Earth extends upward for a very limited distance, and no ordinary flying machine will function in a vacuum. This limitation does not apply to a rocket, which works according to the principle of reaction: every action has an equal and opposite reaction. As gas is sent out through the rocket exhaust, so the vehicle itself is propelled in the opposite direction. The principle is exactly the same as that of the firework display rocket, though for space-probes a charge of gunpowder is replaced by a vast, immensely complicated rocket motor powered, in the main, by liquid propellants.

Rocket research

Rocket research was undertaken in Germany in the decade before the Second World War by men such as Willy Ley and Wernher von Braun, and the first really effective high-altitude rockets, the V2 weapons, came from the Peenemünde station in the Baltic. After the war, many of the German team went to the United States to continue their scientific research. The captured V2's were put to good use. In 1949 a compound arrangement known as a step-vehicle was launched from the proving ground at White Sands. It consisted of a V2 carrying a smaller rocket, a WAC Corporal, which was given a 'running jump' into space and reached the then record height of over 144 miles.

Meanwhile, rocket work was going on in the Soviet Union. On October 4, 1957 the Russians achieved a startling success; they launched Sputnik I, the first man-made moon or artificial satellite in all history. It was a tiny thing, only about the size of a football, but it marked the opening of the Space Age. As it sped round the world, sending back its 'Bleep! bleep!' signals, nobody could doubt that the Moon was within reach.

Satellites of many kinds followed Sputnik I. Up to now most of them have been Russian or American, though small satellites have also been launched by Britain, Japan, China and France. The satellites have contributed immensely to our knowledge of the Earth itself and of the universe. The detection of the all-important Van Allen zones of intense radiation around the Earth is only one of the many discoveries which the satellites have made possible.

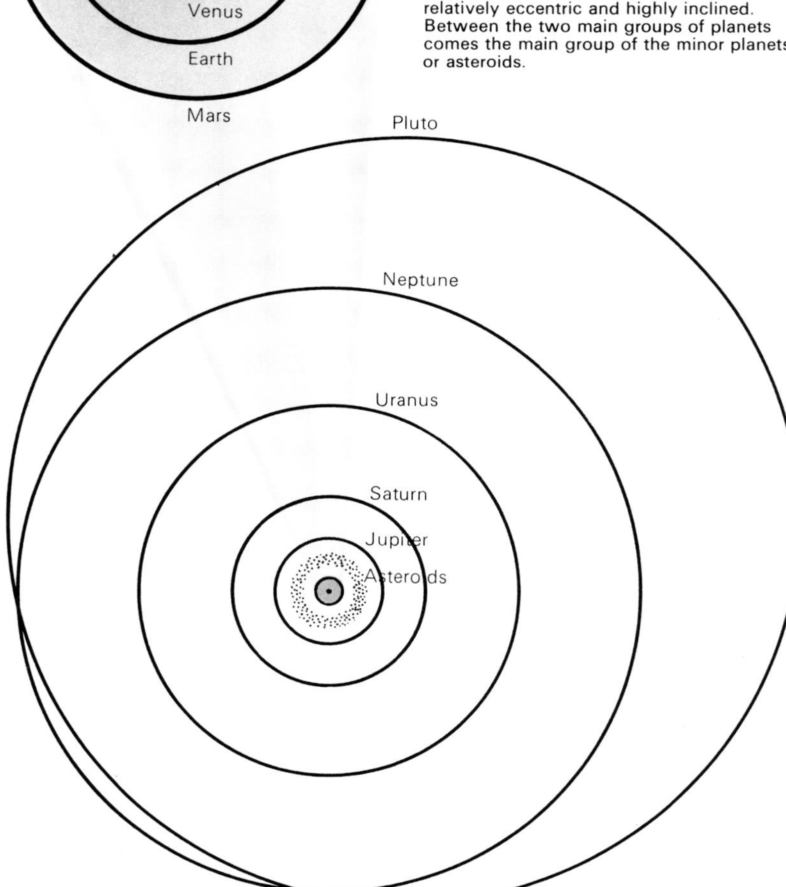

The planets of our Solar System *left*
The inner planets: Mercury, Venus, the Earth and Mars. *Below* The outer planets: Jupiter, Saturn, Uranus, Neptune and Pluto. The distances from the Sun range from an average of 36,000,000 miles for Mercury out to over 3,500,000,000 miles for Pluto. It is clear that the System is divided into two distinct parts; the inner planets are relatively small, and are essentially of the same type as the Earth, while the four giants are gaseous, at least in their outer layers. Pluto is something of a mystery; it is apparently no larger than Mars, and has an exceptional orbit, relatively eccentric and highly inclined. Between the two main groups of planets comes the main group of the minor planets or asteroids.

Men in space

Just as the Russians had launched the first artificial satellite, so they sent up the first man into space: Yuri Gagarin, who made his flight on April 12, 1961. Though he completed only one circuit of the Earth, his journey silenced the critics who had claimed that an astronaut would be at once affected by what fiction-writers commonly called space-sickness, due to the condition of zero gravity. Gagarin was followed by other space-travellers from the U.S.S.R. and the U.S.A.; and it is significant that the first American venture into space was made by Alan Shepard, who, less than ten years later, set foot upon the Moon.

As the 1960s passed by, the original single-passenger space-vehicles were replaced by larger and more complicated craft, carrying two men (as with the Gemini vehicles) or even three (as with some of the Russian space-ships). Docking manœuvres were successfully carried out, as were what are usually called 'space-walks'. Of course there were tragedies. Three American astronauts – Grissom, White and Chaffee – were killed at Cape Kennedy after a disastrous fire in a capsule which was being tested on the ground; and not many weeks later Vladimir Komarov, a veteran Russian cosmonaut, crashed to his death when returning from a space-flight. Then, in 1971, came the tragic deaths of Cosmonauts Dobrovolsky, Volkov and Patsayev, who had spent over three weeks in the massive space-station Salyut; their capsule landed gently, but the three passengers were dead. Their fate was a grim reminder that space is an alien environment, and that the risks of entering it are great indeed.

International co-operation

Salyut was the first true space-laboratory. Meantime the Americans had been planning Skylab, an ambitious research base which would orbit the Earth and would be manned by relays of crews, each of which would remain in the base for a number of weeks.

For the first decade of practical space research, the American and Soviet programmes continued quite independently, with very little co-operation or exchange of information. Clearly this state of affairs is undesirable; and in 1971 NASA made the welcome announcement that a joint space mission was planned, possibly as on the next page. Our picture shows what may become reality within a few years. At a casual glance there seems nothing strange about the two vehicles docking in space – but closer inspection shows that although the craft look 'well-matched', one is American while the other is Russian. The U.S. station is a Skylab, and docking with it is a Soviet Soyuz.

Skylab is made up essentially of hardware of the type used in the Apollo lunar mission. The orbital workshop is a modified Saturn IVb stage, attached to which are solar panels to provide the power, an airlock module and multiple docking adapter, and an Apollo Telescope mount, which has its own cross-shaped solar array wings. Travelling in an almost circular orbit 235 nautical miles above the ground, at an inclination of 50 degrees, the spacecraft – their navigation lights glowing – have left the Earth's shadow (moving right to left in the picture) and are about to pass over the Nile Valley and the Red Sea, which are crossed by a band of cirrus cloud. An Apollo Command Service Module stands a little way off in space, photographing the historic scene.

If this collaboration is achieved (and there is no reason to be pessimistic), then there must be collaboration, too, in journeys to the Moon and to the planets. Not only America and Russia are involved; in particular, some of the equipment which has been widely used is of British design. As space research becomes more and more ambitious, it must also become more and more international.

Artificial satellites marked our first forays into space; manned orbital probes came next. At the same time, the Moon had become the object of attention. The first unmanned lunar probes were sent up by the Russians in 1959, and ten years later came that never-to-be-forgotten moment when Neil Armstrong and Edwin Aldrin stepped out on to the bleak rocks of the Moon.

The Moon had to be our first target. Beyond come the planets, and in this book we shall deal with them in the sequence they are most likely to be visited by the explorers of space. Unmanned probes have already landed on Mars and on Venus. We have come a long way since 1957, when the first tiny artificial satellite made its epic journey.

A look into the future *right*
This scene may become reality before 1975. An American Skylab, or space laboratory, is seen docking with a Soviet Soyuz probe, which acts as a ferry to take crew-members to and from the orbital station. Skylab is very unlike the conventional idea of a wheel-shaped space-station, as planned thirty years ago by Wernher von Braun and others; it is based essentially upon 'hardware' of the type used in Apollo missions. An Apollo module is seen some way off.

NASA
UNITED STATES
CCCP

SPACE STATION

Just as the 1950s and the 1960s saw the steady development of rocket probes and artificial satellites, so the 1970s and the 1980s will see the development of massive orbital space-stations. They represent the next phase of Man's advance beyond the Earth, and by now detailed plans have been drawn up. Russia's Salyut, and the U.S. Skylab, may be regarded as pioneer attempts; and despite the tragedy of Soyuz 11, when the first Salyut crew met with disaster after spending more than three weeks on the space-station, the outlook is encouraging for permanently orbiting laboratories and observatories.

The space-stations will be used primarily as research bases, and all branches of science will benefit immeasurably. Yet there is another aspect to be borne in mind. Future orbital stations may well be used as starting-bases for interplanetary flights to Mars, Venus and beyond. We are no longer bound to our home planet.

When scientific rocket research began, as long ago as the years before the last war, it was both expensive and wasteful. A rocket could be used only once. It was launched; it spent a very brief period in the upper atmosphere, and then it fell back to the ground, destroying itself and often also destroying the equipment which it carried. This limitation persisted with the V2's which were taken to America after 1945, and also with other scientific rockets such as the Vikings. What was needed, of course, was a vehicle which would stay aloft for a protracted period, sending back its findings; and this was achieved with the artificial satellites launched from 1957 onward.

At that time the so-called 're-entry problem' was regarded as one of the most difficult in astronautics. If a spacecraft comes back into the Earth's atmosphere too quickly, it will burn away in the manner of a meteor. The velocity of re-entry must be exactly right. In the event, the problem was solved surprisingly quickly; but it was still true to say that undue waste was involved, since no vehicle could make more than a single flight into space. Clearly, the next step was to produce a vehicle which could be used over and over again.

The space shuttle

This would be not only desirable, but absolutely necessary if it were planned to send up an orbital station to be manned by crews able to carry out tours of duty averaging several weeks in length. Accordingly, the Americans set out to design what is known generally as the space shuttle, able to ferry crews to and from an orbital base. It seems clear that the Russians were planning along the same lines, and with the new spirit of co-operation between the two programmes it is now likely that by 1990, if not before, all shuttles will be international. Unless there are any unforeseen complications, the American shuttle should be operational by 1980, and on January 6, 1972 President Nixon gave official approval to the scheme.

Our picture shows a busy scene in space, some time in the late 1980s. Below can be seen the delta-winged shuttle itself, which is placed into an Earth orbit by a recoverable booster of similar design. Neither is limited to a single trip; indeed, it is hoped that both can be used hundreds of times. This will cause a vast reduction on the overall cost, and will place space research on a really economical footing.

The vehicles will have many rôles to play. For instance, they will be able to carry up relatively large satellites and put them into orbit. They will also be able to inspect and repair others – something which still cannot be done in 1972; if a satellite goes wrong for some reason or other, and ceases to transmit, it has to be 'written off'. Such failures have occurred many times, again causing waste in both time and money.

However, the main function of the shuttles will be to deliver propellant modules for lunar or planetary missions and, above all, to ferry crews to the orbital stations and back home. In the painting, one shuttle has delivered a propellant module for a manned nuclear space-craft, one of two preparing for a voyage to Mars; the nearer shuttle is firing its retro-rockets for return to Earth.

The space station

The station shown here, based on a recent McDonnell-Douglas study, is a development of the Skylab. It is assembled, in a 270-nautical mile orbit, from modules launched by powerful two-stage vehicles. It will accommodate 50, then up to 100 technicians and scientists of all disciplines. Because of the potential hazards of long periods under zero gravity, the station is designed to rotate. Zero gravity conditions will prevail at the hub, but 'artificial gravity' will be provided on other parts of the station; it will spin once every 15 seconds at a radius of 100 feet, but large portions will be contra-rotated to facilitate docking, and for scientific experiments which have to be carried out under conditions of complete weightlessness. Other modules and experiments can be attached as required, while yet others – shown to the right – are free-flying because they require very accurate pointing or very low gravity levels. The main station is, of course, nuclear-powered, and contains a closed life-support system.

To list all the uses of the station would take many pages. One, of practical importance, is brought out in the painting. As we can detect, the clouds show the pattern of a depression. Before the Space Age, meteorology was a delightfully uncertain science, because all observations had to be made from below the atmosphere; it was impossible to gain anything like an overall picture. From space, however, whole weather systems can be studied, and their behaviour interpreted. Many lives have already been saved in this way; dangerous tropical storms far out at sea have been photographed from weather satellites, and people who live in the affected coastal zones have been given ample warning. From the manned space-station a continuous 'storm patrol' will be maintained.

Research from space

The Earth's atmosphere contains protective layers which screen off many of the radiations which bombard us from space. From our point of view this is just as well, as some of them are dangerous; but the screening imposes severe limitations on both astronomers and physicists. From the orbital station they will be able to study the whole range of frequencies. Neither must medical research be neglected; indeed, this may prove to be one of the most important aspects of the entire programme. It is even possible that surgical operations impossible to perform on Earth will be carried out under the zero-gravity environment of the space-station.

There are, however, two aspects which must be considered. First, there are the possibilities of using space-stations for military purposes. We may hope that before elaborate orbital bases are set up the fear of global war will have receded; in any case, it seems that the military rôle of a space-station will be limited to reconnaissance. Much less under our control is the question of how the human body will react to conditions in space. Screening the harmful radiations must be carried out, particularly at times when the Sun is particularly active and both radiations and high-velocity particles are sent out from the violent 'solar storms'. Solar maxima occur about every 11 years; the next is due near 1980.

Most of all, we must find out whether an astronaut will be harmed permanently after staying under reduced or zero gravity conditions for periods of more than a week or two. If the hazard is a real one, methods will have to be found to counteract it; but so far as we can tell at the moment there is no reason for pessimism.

If all goes well, then before the end of our century there will be many massive space-stations orbiting the world; in our skies they will become as familiar as the Sun, the Moon and the stars. They, above all, will represent the triumph of Man's ingenuity, and his ability to conquer all obstacles which stand in the way of scientific progress. More than that: we may regard them as the bases which will lead us on to the exploration of other worlds.

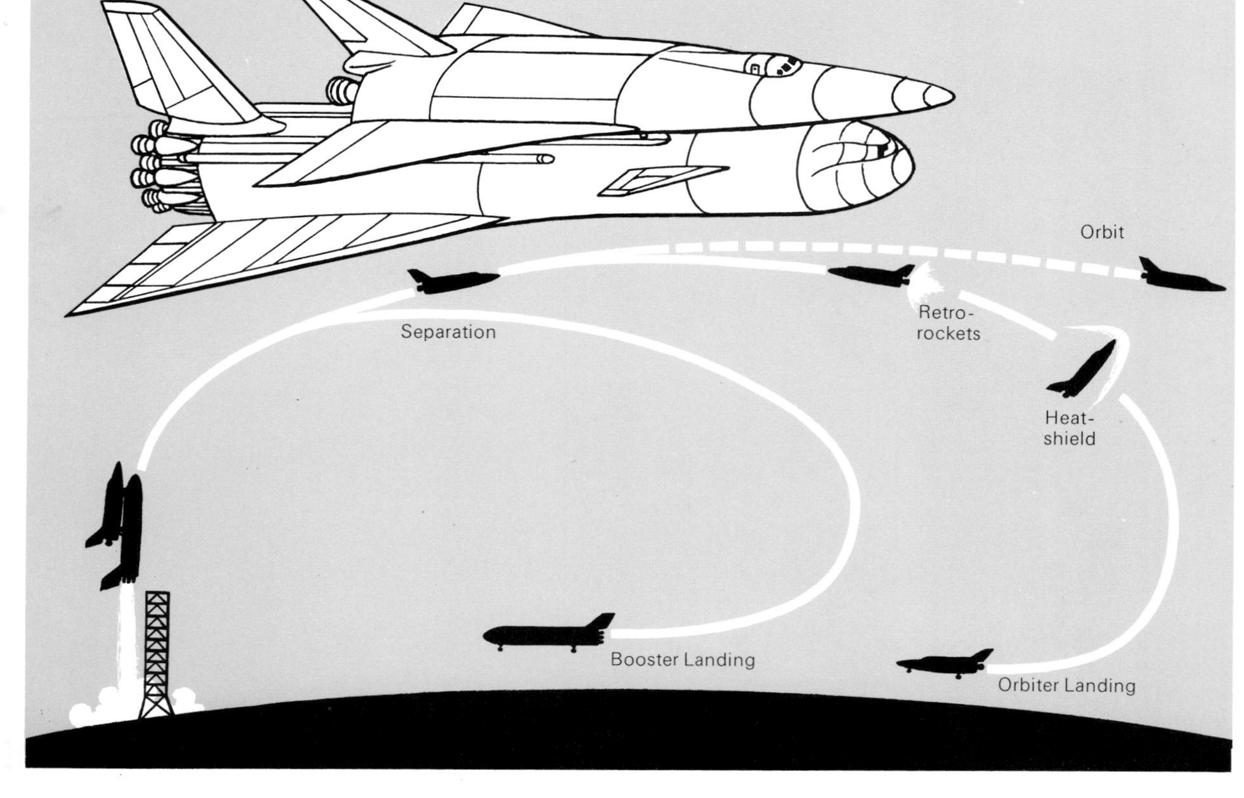

The space shuttle *below*
The shuttle spacecraft and its booster vehicle, both designed for continual re-use. The orbiting shuttle vehicle has two engines, carries two crew, and has capacity for passengers or cargo.

An orbiting space-station *right*
The station moves in an almost circular path at a height of 270 nautical miles above ground level; it can accommodate up to 100 crew-members. Below, we see a shuttle which has delivered a propellant module for a space-ship bound for Mars. The nearer shuttle is just firing its retro-rockets for return to Earth. Both shuttles will be re-usable, perhaps for hundreds of journeys into space; they are delta-winged, since, unlike 'pure' space-craft, they have to be designed so as to fly and manœuvre in the Earth's atmosphere as well as in a vacuum. These shuttles are based on recent design studies by North American Rockwell with the British Aircarft Corporation.

USA

MOON BASE

On July 21, 1969, the first men from Earth stepped out on to the barren rocks of the Moon. Apollo 11 marked the greatest triumph of the programme which had been initiated so many years earlier; it showed that man could not only reach the Moon, but could survive there.

The Moon is not a very friendly world. Airless, waterless and lifeless, it offers little comfort to colonists from Earth. Yet it represents both an ideal site for a scientific research base, and a stepping-stone to the planets. Our exploration of deep space can only begin with the Moon.

The Moon is a smaller world than the Earth. Its diameter is only 2,160 miles, and it has a mass of only 1/81 of that of our world. This means that it has a lower escape velocity (1.5 miles per second) and a lower surface gravity; an astronaut on the Moon has only one-sixth of his Earth weight. Walking on the Moon is easy enough, as has been amply demonstrated by the Apollo astronauts, but prolonged exertion is tiring.

During the 1960s the first really accurate maps of the Moon were drawn up, from the photographs sent back by the Orbiter probes. These maps covered both the familiar hemisphere of the Moon and also the far hemisphere, which is never visible from Earth because it is always turned away from us. Then came the pioneer landings, and the first automatic lunar transmitting stations.

Fears had been expressed that the lunar surface might be too soft and dusty to be safe for manned exploration. These fears have not been justified; the rocks of the Moon are pleasingly firm, and there is no reason to suppose that treacherous regions exist.

Originally it was thought that because of the Moon's lack of atmosphere, meteoric bombardment might make it necessary to build a base underground, but this does not now seem to be the case. Probably the pioneer base will look rather like a group of cylinders or Antarctic survey huts; at first the living accommodation will be inside a grounded space-station which had formerly been in orbit round the Moon. This sort of base may well be established within the next ten years. It will not be permanently manned, but will be able to support crews who will stay in it for a period of weeks or even months at a time. Again, it is to be hoped that the base will be international.

The Moon as seen from the Earth. *right*
The broad dark plains are known as 'seas', even though they are waterless; the Moon is a world of lava-plains, mountains, peaks and craters of all sizes.

The advanced base

From these humble beginnings, Man will plan a much more elaborate lunar colony; and our next picture shows a scene on the Moon during the twenty-first century. We are looking down several thousand feet into a small crater near the Moon's north pole, where a permanent base has been set up. The larger dome is multi-storied, and contains the living quarters; above it is an optical telescope, and around it are the transparent tubes which make up the lunar 'farm'. Hydroponic methods will be very important on the Moon; the plants are nourished by liquids circulating beneath them. Even with the improved methods of transport between the Earth and the Moon, every effort must be made to make the lunar colony as self-supporting as possible. Oxygen and water can be produced by processing the lunar surface materials, as shown by the apparatus to the left of the dome. Other domes contain laboratories, equipment of all kinds, and stores. In the foreground, a 'crawler' vehicle is collecting samples from the inner slopes of the crater.

Though the Moon is so different from the Earth in its condition, it is made of essentially the same materials; the rocks are of the basaltic variety, and no unknown substances have been found there. Whether there will be any materials of sufficient commercial value to be ferried home seems doubtful. But to the geologist, as well as to the astronomer, the Moon is an ideal site for research. Since the lunar atmosphere was lost many thousands of millions of years ago, there has been virtually no erosion; the Moon's surface looks the same now as it did before the time when the Earth was ruled by giant dinosaurs.

Though the Moon's surface does show slight tremors, powerful 'moonquakes' belong to the remote past, and there is no danger that the lunar bases will be shaken down. Neither do meteoritic falls appear potentially very dangerous, even though the Moon has no atmosphere to act as a screen. On the other hand, the surface is exposed to all the various radiations coming from space; and protective methods to counter radiation effects will have to be devised.

Of course, the main disadvantage of the Moon is its lack of air, and the fear of a leak in the base will be ever-present in the colonists' minds. However, there will be no difficulties in communicating with the Earth, and there will be many artificial lunar satellites to act as radio and television relays between the different bases on the Moon itself.

Research activity

Life in the lunar colony will be full of interest. The Earth, looming large in the lunar sky, seems very far away; it will seem to stay almost motionless in the heavens, with the background of brilliant, untwinkling stars sweeping slowly past it. Astronomers living on the Moon will have great advantages; optical telescopes will not be handicapped by having to look through a layer of unsteady, obscuring atmosphere, and neither will radio telescopes be limited. Moreover, the lower surface gravity means that in some ways it will be easier to build large pieces of equipment, and this will be of particular use with radio telescopes, which have to be of considerable size. On the other hand there there are great ranges of temperature on the Moon – from above +210 degrees Fahrenheit at noon down to −250 degrees Fahrenheit at midnight on the lunar equator, though near the Moon's pole the daytime heat will be much less. Great care must be taken in the choice of materials which will be exposed to these changes in temperature. But these difficulties will be overcome; the permanent lunar base will become reality, perhaps in our own time.

The pioneer lunar base *left*
This may well be set up within the next couple of decades. In the foreground we see the basic space-station module, placed on the lunar surface by the propulsion module of a 'space tug' similar to the one seen landing on the right. The grounded station can accommodate a crew of twelve, and can provide everything necessary for a prolonged stay. Behind is a cargo-landing craft, together with a separate cargo module. At the extreme right is a lunar drill, and in the right foreground is a 'Moon Rover' for long-range exploration. The bright 'star' to the left of the crescent Earth is Venus.

A permanent lunar base *right*
Near the Moon's North Pole, where the daytime temperature is much lower than at sites closer to the equator – though the nights are equally cold. In addition to the main dome, containing the living quarters, there are various others, used for equipment and storage. Each dome has its separate system of air-locks. In this scene the Earth has just passed through the Milky Way into the constellation of Gemini, the Twins. The red star to the right is the semi-regular variable star Eta Geminorum, shown at its maximum of just below the third magnitude.

MARS

Beyond the Moon we come to the red planet Mars – perhaps the most fascinating of all the worlds in the Sun's family. Though it is slightly more distant than Venus, it has always been regarded as our second space-target, because even though it is a cold planet with a painfully thin atmosphere it is still more Earthlike than any other body in the Solar System. There is always the chance that it may not be entirely hostile to all forms of life.

Unmanned probes have already reached Mars; there is every expectation that men will follow before the turn of the century, and that in the coming years we will see the establishment of a full-scale Martian base. If so, we will have a vantage point on the outskirts of the inner part of the Solar System; beyond Mars lies the asteroid belt, and then, far away, the giant planets. We would be justified in describing Mars as 'a frontier world'.

Mars and the Earth compared. *above*
Earth has a diameter of 7,926 miles; Mars, only 4,200 miles. The escape velocity is much lower (3.1 miles per second), and the mass only one-tenth of that of the Earth.

Is there life on Mars? This is a question which has been asked for many centuries, and which even now cannot be finally answered. In 1908 Percival Lowell, one of America's great astronomers, published a book in which he claimed that Mars was inhabited by advanced beings who had built a gigantic irrigation system to draw every scrap of water from their arid planet; who has not heard of the Martian canals? Even though we no longer believe in Martians, it is not impossible that the Red Planet supports organisms of a kind; and this is one of the reasons why it is so intriguing.

With its diameter of 4,200 miles, and its mass of only one-tenth that of the Earth, Mars is one of the smallest planets in the Solar System. Only Mercury and perhaps Pluto are inferior to it. The escape velocity is 3.1 miles per second – sufficient to retain only a tenuous atmosphere. The existence of an atmosphere has long been known and clouds and dust-storms are not uncommon.

Telescopically, Mars shows a reddish disk, with dark markings here and there, and whitish caps covering the poles. It has always been tempting to believe that the caps are due to some icy or frosty deposit, and that the dark regions are vegetation. Certainly there is a seasonal cycle, controlled by the more or less regular increase and decrease of the polar caps. The tilt of Mars' axis is almost the same as that of Earth, so that the seasons are of the same basic type; but they are much longer, since the Martian year amounts to 687 Earth-days. The 'day', however, is 24 hours 37 minutes – only about half an hour longer than our own.

Exploratory probes

The first successful probe to Mars was Mariner 4, of 1965. It was a fly-by, and made only one close approach to the planet, but it was highly successful, and sent back spectacular pictures showing that instead of having a flat landscape Mars, like the Moon, is cratered. Some of the craters are extremely large, and show signs of erosion – as is only to be expected upon a world which has appreciable atmosphere. Even more important were the measurements sent back of the atmospheric density. Just before Mariner 4 passed behind Mars, as seen from Earth, its radio signals came to us after having passed through the Martian atmosphere. The amount by which these signals were distorted gave a clue to the amount of atmosphere responsible – and the results were surprising! The ground pressure on Mars seems to be no more than 6 to 7 millibars; that is to say, equivalent to the pressure in our own air at over 100,000 feet above sea-level. And instead of being composed of nitrogen, the atmosphere of Mars seems to be made up chiefly of carbon dioxide.

These results were confirmed by the next two fly-by Mariners, 6 and 7, which went past Mars in 1969, only a few days after the Apollo 11 landing on the Moon. Further spectacular pictures were obtained, showing the Martian craters.

The next steps were taken in 1971. The Americans launched two probes. Of these, Mariner 8 failed, but Mariner 9 entered a closed path round Mars, and sent back further information. When it first arrived in the region of the planet, Mars was experiencing one of its major dust-storms; the progress of this storm is shown on the four drawings below. The storm began in early October; when Mariner 9 entered its closed orbit, in late November, little of the surface was visible. Before long, however, the dust cleared, and the surface features could again be seen. The exact nature of these dust-storms is rather uncertain; presumably they are due to material whipped up from the red 'deserts' by winds.

Martian landing

Russian probes reached Mars at about the same time, and both entered closed orbits. One probe deposited a Soviet pennant on the planet's surface. The other landed a capsule, using a combination of rocket braking and parachutes. The touch-down was carried out successfully, but unfortunately the transmitters in the capsule failed within half a minute of landing, so that no useful information was obtained.

Because the Martian atmosphere is so thin, parachutes are of limited use, and this makes soft landings decidedly difficult. The procedure to be adopted for the U.S. Viking, to be launched in 1974, is necessarily complicated. The 'Lander', not too unlike the lunar Surveyors of the 1960s, is carried initially in a protective aerodynamic shell. In our painting, it is shown as its retro-rockets are being fired. The time and distance scales have been condensed, in order to show the operation and still keep both vehicles in view; but the principles are clear enough.

The aeroshell is jettisoned, and the Lander descends to the surface, using rocket braking as well as parachutes. When it has landed, it will be capable of sending back information of all kinds; it will measure the temperatures, the wind-speeds and any possible surface tremors, and it will be able to scoop up samples of Martian crust, analyzing it and probably finding out, once and for all, whether any form of life exists there. Meantime, the Orbiter section of the Viking continues in its path round Mars, acting as a relay between the Lander and the controllers on Earth. In the painting, a dust-storm is shown obscuring part of the planet's surface to the upper right; the sharp haze layer near the limb is also noticeable.

'Life or no life'

Great care is taken to sterilize all parts of the Viking which are scheduled to land on Mars. This is because on a planet with an atmosphere – even a tenuous one – terrestrial bacteria might be able to survive, and even multiply. If any bacteria were carried to Mars, future expeditions would be unable to decide which organisms were indigenous to the planet and which were not. From a scientific point of view this would be disastrous. Caution must also be exercised in bringing Martian samples back to Earth, as will no doubt become possible within the next few years. The chances of bringing home any dangerous contaminants may be slight, but they are not nil, and the risk is not justifiable. Samples from the Mars expedition will be landed on our world only when scientists are satisfied that there is nothing harmful in them.

Viking will be significant inasmuch as it will presumably clear up the problem of 'life or no life'. Now that we know the real thinness of the atmosphere, the vegetation theory of the dark areas seems less attractive than it used to do in the days before Mariner 4; it is quite likely that the polar caps are made up not of ordinary snow or ice, but of solid carbon dioxide. However, at the beginning of February 1972 information from Mariner 9 made it almost certain that water and its erosion effects are present.

Following Viking, a probable next step will be to soft-land a probe on Mars and then bring it back. It may also be possible to operate an automatic 'Mars crawler', built upon the pattern of the Lunokhod I vehicle which explored the Moon throughout most of 1971. There is, of course, one complication. Light, or a radio signal, can travel from the Earth to the Moon in $1\frac{1}{4}$ seconds; but Mars is over 100 times as remote even when at its nearest to us, so that the time-lag will be appreciable. There will be a noticeable delay between the transmission of a signal, or an order, and its arrival at Mars.

Four views of Mars *below*
Based on drawings made by Patrick Moore with his 12.5-inch reflector at Selsey. These drawings show the progress of the great dust-storm which obscured large areas of Mars at the time of the arrival in Martian orbit of the U.S. probe Mariner 9.
September 20; the storm has not begun.
October 4; the detail is blurred.
November 1; little detail is seen.
December 8; a clearing has begun.

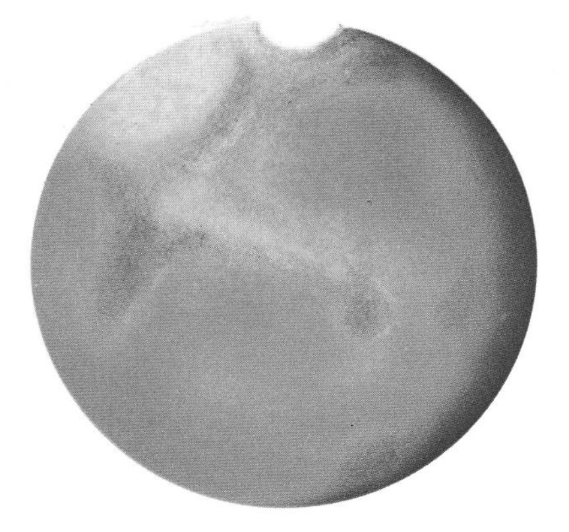

20 September 1971

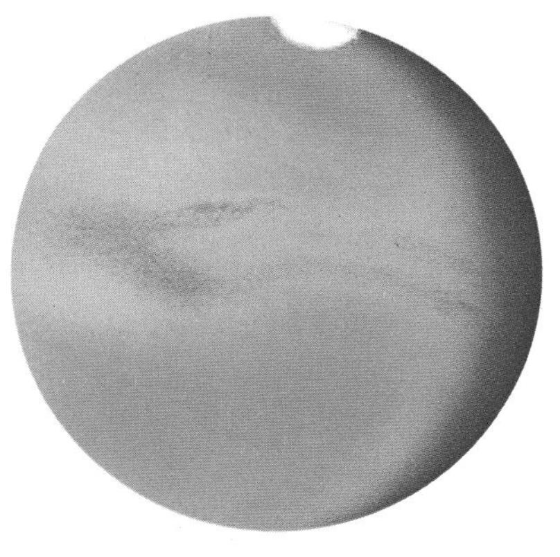

4 October 1971

1 November 1971

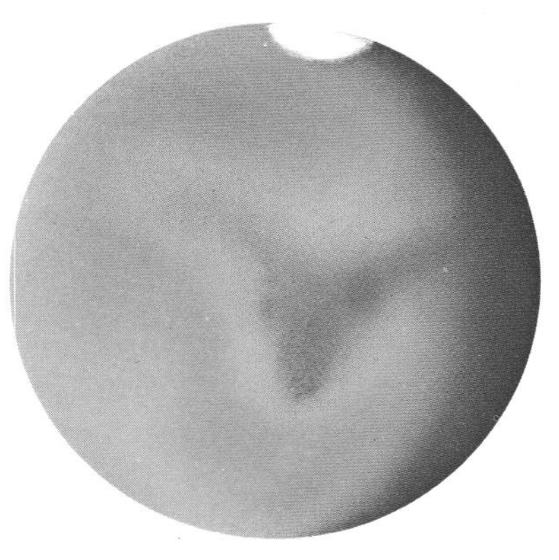

8 December 1971

Viking to Mars *right*
To be launched in 1974, and reach Mars in 1975. The orbiting section will enter a closed path round the planet, and will act as a communications relay for the Lander, which will go down on to the surface. In this view the retro-rockets are being fired. To show the whole operation, both time and distance scales have been compressed in this painting, but the principles of the operation are clear. The same sort of procedure was used by the Russians in their partially-successful probe Mars 3 in 1971.

MARS 2

Martian crater *right*
Computer-enhanced photographs from Mariner 9 reveal crater rims that are similar to collapsed craters found on volcanoes on earth. The large crater is located near Nodus Gordii (the Gordian Knot). It is 70 miles (112 km.) in diameter and equal in size to the largest comparable features on earth.

By our present-day standards the problems of setting up a base on Mars are very great. The main difficulty lies in the sheer distance of the planet. Even at its nearest, Mars never approaches us much within 35,000,000 miles, and a journey there by chemically-propelled rockets lasts for months. Even with the nuclear rockets which are now being planned, and which should be fully operational by the 1980s, the time of travel will still be a matter of weeks; and this is very different from the local journey to the Moon, where a landing can always be abandoned if there are technical difficulties (as did actually happen with Apollo 13, in 1970).

Also, it is still uncertain how an astronaut will react to long periods of reduced or zero gravity, as must be experienced on the way to Mars. Therefore we cannot yet give a definite date to the first attempt at setting up a base there; but if the pioneer journey is made around 1990, it is logical to assume that a base will exist before 2050. It may well be set up considerably earlier than this.

The terrain

The terrain is not flat or undulating, as used to be thought; the pictures from the first Mariners show this clearly. Some of the craters appear to be of volcanic origin, though it is not certain whether any active vulcanism persists on Mars. It is not now generally believed that the dark areas are depressions (ocean basins?) as used to be thought; some of them, including the famous V-shaped marking known as the Syrtis Major, are elevated. They are somewhat warmer than the reddish 'deserts', but the Martian climate is very chill. At noon on the equator, a thermometer would show about +70 degrees Fahrenheit, but the midnight temperature always drops to below −100 degrees Fahrenheit, since the thin atmosphere is poor at retaining warmth.

The Martian base

In the picture, it is assumed that the Martian base is to be set up near the edge of a dark area bordered by hills. This is logical, since it will provide the best variety of surface for geological studies. We are looking north-west, away from the rising Sun. The nearer of Mars' two dwarf satellites, Phobos, has risen in the west and is now near the centre of the sky-area.

The large, high-gain antenna to the left is aimed directly at the Earth, though messages can also be relayed via orbiting stations. No difficulties will be experienced in keeping in touch with Earth when the planets are suitably positioned, though the conditions will become very difficult at times when Earth and Mars are on opposite sides of the Sun. The permanent base, shown at the top left, is being assembled from the halves of cylindrical units landed by the descent stage of the Martian excursion module. A complete MEM is visible in the foreground. Initially, the cylinders can be used as self-contained living units; if re-erected horizontally they could be extended below ground if required.

The excursion module is one of several likely to be in the area; they are used to land the astronauts on Mars. Most of the top section lifts off for return to Mars orbit, where a space-station and a shuttle are waiting. In addition to providing temporary accommodation, the descent stage has a hangar for a Rover, which is seen to the right; this is used for exploring the surrounding area.

Small craters may be seen, pitting the surface here and there, though on the whole Mars is rather less rough than the Moon. There are clouds, though very different from the billowing clouds of Earth; little rain may have fallen on Mars for many millions of years.

The atmosphere

An essential feature of this or any other Martian base is its system of air-locks. It is true that Mars has an atmosphere; but the thin carbon-dioxide 'air', so unlike ours, is of little practical use except possibly as a shield against some meteors. It may even be very inefficient as a protection against dangerous short-wave radiations. It cannot possibly be breathed by any life-form built upon our own pattern, and it is true to say that so far as the astronauts are concerned it might as well not be there. There is no chance that a colonist will be able to go out into the open wearing no protective clothing other than breathing equipment, as used to be thought when it was believed that the surface atmospheric pressure was of the order of 85 millibars. Full pressure suiting will be necessary all the time, just as it is in space or on the Moon.

Much depends upon whether there are any useful materials to be found on Mars, either on the surface or below the crust. If water existed, in the form of ice, the problems of the colonists would be greatly eased; and though this may be regarded as rather unlikely, it is not out of the question.

Because of the greater distance, a colony on Mars will have to become to all intents and purposes self-supporting at a very early stage; there can be no 'breaking-in' period, as with the Moon. Tours of duty there will also have to be considerably longer. Fortunately the surface gravity is greater than with the Moon, and amounts to approximately one-third of that of the Earth, which is almost certainly tolerable for an indefinite period.

From Mars, the Earth will be visible as a bright, bluish starlike object, moving rather as Venus does to us; it will be seen in the east before dawn or in the west after sunset. When the two planets are at their closest, a Martian observer will be unable to see the Earth at all, because it will be between Mars and the Sun, and its dark face will be presented. Occasionally, of course, it will pass in transit against the Sun, and will then be seen as a black spot against the brilliant solar disk.

The Martian scene depicted here is likely to become reality at some time during the next century. It seems certain that Mars will become the third inhabited world in the Solar System, following the Earth and its Moon.

The Martian base *right*
Seen after the first colony is established. The Martian Excursion Module, used to carry the astronauts on to the planet, is shown in the foreground; in the distance is another module of the same kind, and there will be others in the area. The base itself is being assembled from the two cylindrical halves. To the left is the powerful radio antenna aimed at the Earth, while to the far right is seen a Martian roving vehicle, an advanced version of the lunar roving vehicle first used in 1971 by the astronauts of Apollo 15.

MARS 3

Mars is a strange, rugged world – in some ways intermediate between the Earth and the Moon. The picture of a tolerably warm planet, with abundant water supplies in the form of polar snow and with great tracts of vegetation, has long since been abandoned; the famous canals have proved to be nothing more significant than elevated ridges or chains of roughly-aligned craters.

When astronauts go there, they will find much that is unfamiliar. The scene shown in the painting below is typical of one of the rougher areas. It is true that the eroded rock mass to the right is only a few hundred feet high; Mars has no mountain-chains comparable with the terrestrial Rockies or the lunar Apennines, but there are many peaks, some of them appreciable. The scene opens out on to a relatively smooth area, though pitted with craters. This is one of the so-called deserts of Mars, but there is little resemblance to an Earth-desert such as the Sahara or Death Valley. The climate is cold; the deserts are appreciably chillier than the dark areas. A desert on Earth is sandy; but sand is produced by the action of running water, of which there may never have been much on Mars. The Martian tracts are covered with some reddish mineral, such as felsite or limonite – oxides of iron: it is also likely that much of the oxygen originally present in the planet's atmosphere has combined with iron in the surface rocks, giving their reddish colour.

Also, Mars must be almost a silent planet. Sound would be very feebly propagated in the tenuous atmosphere, and another interesting fact is that it would never be possible to light a fire in the open – simply because the atmosphere is practically devoid of oxygen for combustion, and of course no flame can burn in carbon dioxide.

In the painting, both the Martian satellites, Phobos and Deimos, are seen in transit across the face of the Sun. Neither can produce a solar eclipse, since both are too small; even Phobos, the larger and nearer of the two, can cover only one-third of the solar disk. It crosses the Sun in only 19 seconds. Deimos is even smaller, and takes two minutes to pass across the Sun. The Earth and Moon are also shown in the painting, appearing as a bright double star. They also can transit the Sun, as will next happen in 1984.

Geologically, Mars should be even more interesting than the Moon, and the pioneer explorers will do all they can to collect samples from various sites on the planet. In the foreground of the painting opposite, an astronaut is collecting rock samples from the inner wall of a crater near the Martian north pole, from which most of the frozen deposit has evaporated. Neither Phobos nor Deimos is shown here; from high Martian latitudes neither satellite can be seen, because both revolve in almost exactly the plane of the planet's equator, and from the polar zones they remain permanently below the horizon.

The polar deposit

The nature of the polar deposit is still not known with certainty. It may well consist mainly of solid carbon dioxide, though it is possible that there is some ordinary snow or ice as well. In Martian winter, a polar cap is very extensive; but it shrinks rapidly during the spring and early summer, and at midsummer the southern cap has been known to vanish entirely. The northern cap always persists, though it may become very small. On Mars, as on Earth, southern summer occurs when the planet is near perihelion, so that the southern hemisphere climate is more extreme; the summers are shorter but hotter, the winters longer and colder. The effects are more noticeable on Mars, partly because the planet's orbit is more eccentric than ours and partly because there is no sea to even out the climates.

Neither is it yet certain whether a polar cap melts during the warmer season, or whether it sublimes: that is to say, changes directly from the solid to the gaseous state. In any case, a haze over the polar caps was recorded on the early Mariner photographs. It is visible in the painting only because of the violet tint that it imparts to the dark sky; it is tenuous, and from ground level it is probably quite transparent. From these latitudes, the Sun is low in the sky, so there are long shadows.

Individual transport

The astronaut in the background of the painting has just taken off on what may be called a one-man flying platform. This is a device which can be used to give greater mobility than ground transport. On Mars, where the atmosphere is so thin, no conventional-type aircraft are of the slightest use; after all, no passenger aircraft so far built can operate at a height of over 100,000 feet above the Earth, and even at this altitude the atmospheric pressure is greater than it is on the surface of Mars. The 'platform' could probably be used up to a range of 25 miles. Communications from one Martian base to another will probably be by means of orbital relays, because it is not likely that the atmosphere of the planet has an ionosphere sufficient to reflect radio waves back to the ground and make direct long-range signalling possible.

What will be the eventual future of bases on Mars? As yet we can only speculate; but it is not unlikely that within the next few centuries there will be thriving colonies there, entirely self-supporting. It is not certain whether a child born on Mars, under the low surface gravity conditions, will ever be able to adapt to conditions on Earth; this is a problem for the future, but it could well be that a separate race of 'Martians' will come into existence. Whether their physical characteristics will, in the still more distant future, differ from those of their terrestrial ancestors remains to be seen.

Past life on Mars

Another problem which will be investigated by the astronauts who land on Mars will be that of possible past life on the planet. We know that there is no advanced life there now, and very probably none has ever existed. Mars, with its weak pull, must have lost most of its atmosphere fairly quickly; life is slow to evolve, and it seems that conditions on Mars must have become hostile before life had sufficient time to develop there. However, lowly life-forms are notoriously hardy, and we know that organisms can survive in what seem to be very unlikely places. It is possible, then, that there has been life on Mars, and in this case the explorers will find traces of it in the surface rocks.

Science-fiction writers have made great play of the idea of giving Mars a new, dense atmosphere, and making it habitable. It can only be said that so far as our present techniques can carry us, any such programme is quite out of the question; but it would be dangerous to claim that it will always be so. One major objection is that even if Mars were miraculously provided with an Earth-type atmosphere, it could not retain it for long on the astronomical scale. But all this is highly speculative, and for the moment at least we must accept Mars as it is: an unfriendly world, and yet a world which holds out exciting possibilities for future colonization. The new 'Martians' will set out within the next few decades.

Polar expedition *right*
This expedition to the polar region may take place before the end of our century, even if a full-scale base on the planet has not then been set up. The polar area is still partly covered with whitish deposit, either solid carbon dioxide or else a mixture of carbon dioxide snow and ordinary snow or ice. One astronaut is collecting rock samples; his colleague has just taken off on a 'flying platform' which will give him a travelling range of up to twenty-five miles. From these high latitudes, neither satellite rises above the horizon at any time.

Martian scene *below*
A rock mass reaches up a few hundreds of feet, while most of the picture is taken up with the reddish-ochre desert land which covers so much of Mars. The Sun shines down less brilliantly than from earth; in front of it appear the black specks of the dwarf Martian satellites, Phobos and Deimos. The Earth and its moon appear conspicuously in the dark-blue sky.

MARS 4

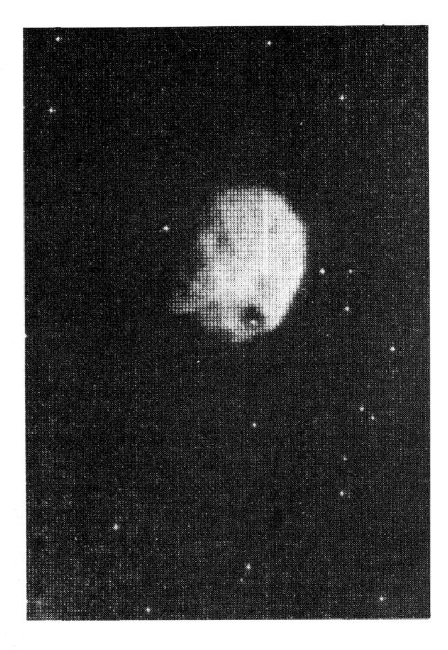

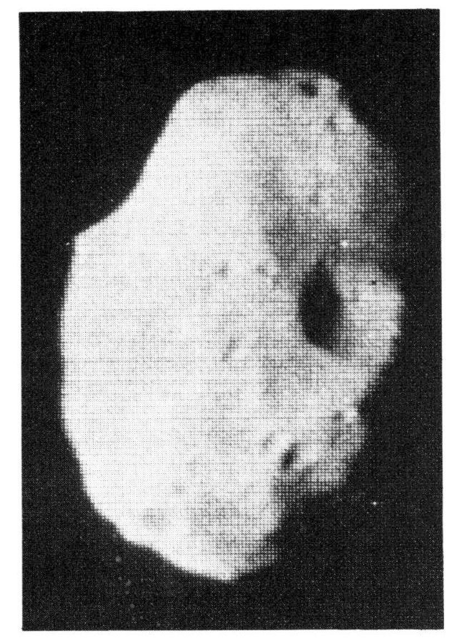

Phobos *above*
First close-up views of the inner Martian moon Phobos: Left from 9175 miles (14680 km.); right from 3460 miles (5540 km.)

One of the most interesting features of Mars is its pair of satellites. Phobos and Deimos, as they are named (after the two mythological attendants of Mars, the War-God) were discovered in 1877 by the American astronomer Asaph Hall. They had not been seen before because both are very small and faint, so that powerful telescopes have to be used in order to show them.

Both satellites revolve virtually in the plane of the planet's equator, which is why they are never visible from the polar regions of Mars. Also, both are close to the ground. Phobos moves at a mean distance of only 5,800 miles from the centre of Mars, which means that it is only 3,700 miles above the surface; the distances for Deimos are 14,600 miles and 12,500 miles respectively. The revolution periods are 7 hours 39 minutes for Phobos and 30 hours 18 minutes for Deimos.

The Martian 'month'

Since Mars has a rotation period of 24 hours 37 minutes, the Martian 'month', as reckoned by Phobos, is shorter than the day! To an observer on the planet, Phobos would seem to rise in the west, cross the sky in a direction opposite to that of the Sun and stars, and set in the east only 4¼ hours later, during which time it would go through more than half its cycle of phases from new to full. The interval between successive risings would be only a little over eleven hours. Moreover, Phobos would seem appreciably larger when high up than when low down. Often it would be eclipsed by the shadow of Mars, and only near midsummer and midwinter would it be free of shadow for the whole of its passage across the sky.

Deimos behaves differently. As Mars spins, Deimos almost keeps pace with it, and as seen from one site on the planet's surface Deimos would remain above the horizon for over 60 consecutive hours, passing twice through its full cycle of phases. Its eclipses would be similar to those of Phobos, though not quite so frequent.

Phobos is unique in the Solar System in that its revolution period is less than the rotation period of its primary. Some years ago, calculations were made indicating that it was spiralling slowly downward, and would hit the planet in 50,000 years from now. From these calculations, the Russian astronomer Shklovskii suggested that Phobos must be being 'braked' by friction with the extremely thin upper part of the Martian atmosphere. This would mean that the mass of Phobos must be negligible, as otherwise the frictional braking would be too slight to be noticed. He went on to propose that Phobos might be nothing more nor less than a hollow space-station launched by the Martians!

Not surprisingly, this theory met with little support, and before long it became clear that the original calculations were wrong; Phobos has a stable orbit and is not spiralling downward. All the same, it is a strange little body, and it began to seem even more curious in 1969, when a close-range photograph from Mariner 7 showed that it is irregular in shape.

Mariner 9

A much closer-range picture was obtained from Mariner 9 in November 1971. The probe was less than 14,000 miles from the satellite, and the details on Phobos were clearly shown. The shape is very irregular, though basically elliptical; the average dimensions are, as expected, about 16 miles by 13 miles. The largest crater shown is over 4 miles across. Whether it is a blowhole crater of internal origin, or whether it is due to a meteoritic impact, is not yet certain.

Phobos looks very much like a 'bit of something' – and this may well be the case. Quite possibly it is not a true satellite, but merely a member of the asteroid belt which came close to Mars in the remote past and was captured. This would admittedly involve some coincidences, particularly since there can be little doubt that Deimos is of the same nature; but at least we may be sure that both dwarf attendants are basically different from our own massive Moon, or from the larger satellites of the giant planets. Evidently it is rocky and very old, and it must have considerable structural strength.

Natural space stations

Suggestions have often been made that Phobos (and Deimos, too) could be pressed into service. The satellites might be regarded as natural space-stations. Their gravitational pulls are very slight; the escape velocity of Phobos is about 30 miles per hour, and that of Deimos rather less. In theory, this is still too high to allow an astronaut to 'jump clear' of the satellite by muscle-power alone; but anyone who leaped upward from Phobos or Deimos would take a very long time to come down, and could well be classed as a temporary independent satellite of Mars!

It is not likely that men will land on either Phobos or Deimos before setting foot on Mars itself. There would be nothing to be gained by making the attempt, which would be extremely difficult from a navigational viewpoint. However, it is very probable that touchdowns will be made there eventually. It will not be a case of a conventional landing manœuvre; it will be much more in the nature of a docking operation, since the tiny gravitational pull of the satellite will be to all intents and purposes inappreciable.

From Deimos, the view of Mars will be magnificent; it is shown in the painting opposite. Mars is seen at half-phase, so that its eroded craters are best seen along the terminator (that is to say, the boundary between the sunlit and the night hemispheres). At the top is the bright south polar cap. Toward the lower right is one of the most interesting features on Mars, the object long known as the Nix Olympica. It is visible from Earth with a moderate-sized telescope when Mars is well placed; it then appears as a small round spot. When photographed from Mariner 7, in 1969, it was found to be a giant 300-mile crater – larger than any of the famous craters of the Moon. Other craters photographed by Mariner 7 are also shown.

As seen from Deimos, Mars would appear to spin very slowly – because, as we have seen, the rotation period of Mars is not much shorter than the period taken by Deimos to complete one circuit of the planet. Closer in, from Phobos, Mars would dominate much of the sky, and would cast a brilliant reddish light on to the irregular rocks and pits of the satellite.

Though we are looking far into the future, the possible use of Phobos and Deimos as space-platforms is worthy of closer consideration. Judging from the Mariner photographs, they are firm, solid bodies with considerable cohesion, and even though their escape velocities are so low there are some scientific experiments in which a very slight pull of gravity might be useful. Also, there is the question of communication. Almost certainly it will be necessary to establish relay satellites round Mars soon after the first bases are set up there (except in the unlikely event of the planet proving to have a useful ionosphere), but a radio station on Deimos, in particular, would be extremely valuable inasmuch as it could give coverage over a full hemisphere of the planet.

The meteorology of Mars

There is, too, the question of the meteorology of Mars. Wind systems occur; moving clouds can be observed even from Earth observatories, and it seems that the dust-storms which occasionally hide the surface must be wind-raised. From Deimos, weather systems could be observed in their entirety, and closer-range studies could be carried out from Phobos, which may not lie very far above the detectable limits of the Martian exosphere (that is to say, the outermost layer of the planet's tenuous atmosphere).

It remains to be seen whether scientific bases on the natural satellites will have any advantages over orbital bases of the Skylab type; but the possibilities are there, and may one day be exploited.

It will also be of the greatest interest to analyze the material of Phobos and Deimos themselves. At present their densities are unknown (the escape velocities given above have been calculated on the assumption that the densities of the satellites are equal to that of Mars itself, which appears to be reasonable). It is not likely that Phobos and Deimos ever formed part of Mars. Either they were produced by material which was once spread round the planet, or else they are captured asteroids. Probably it will be possible to reach them before we can send our probes out into the belt of asteroids, and so they may provide us with our first samples of material from the outer part of the Solar System.

Whether or not we establish relay stations or scientific bases on Phobos or Deimos, it is difficult to doubt that Mars itself will be reached in the foreseeable future. The paintings shown here represent what we believe will be found there; and thanks to the Mariner probes we have a great deal of reliable information to guide us. But we must always remember that Mars has given us plenty of surprises in the past, and may have many more stored up for us in the years to come.

Perhaps we may look back to the words of Percival Lowell, written in 1906. He may have been wrong in his interpretation of the so-called Martian canals, but at least he put forward an idealistic view of the attitude of his 'Martians', whom, he believed, had outlawed warfare and had united in order to make the best of their arid world. There could be no conflict upon Mars. In Lowell's words: 'War is a survival among us from savage times, and affects now chiefly the boyish and unthinking element of the nation. The wisest realize that there are better ways of practising heroism and other and more certain ends of ensuring the survival of the fittest. It is something people outgrow.' Let us hope that we, too, have outgrown it before we set up the first base upon the red deserts of Mars.

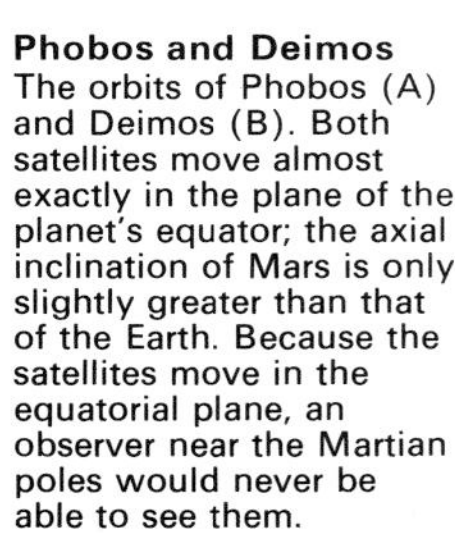

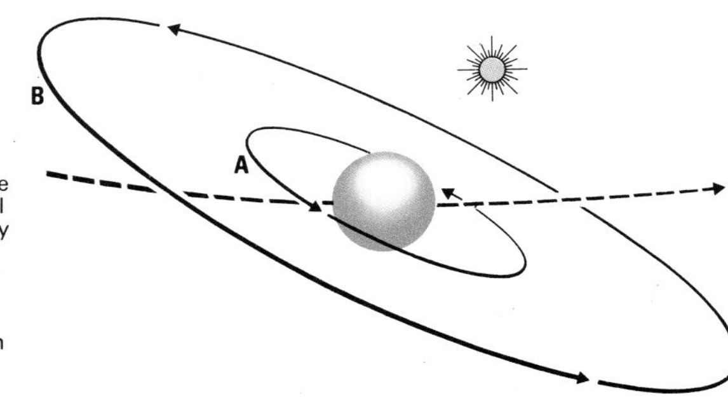

Phobos and Deimos
The orbits of Phobos (A) and Deimos (B). Both satellites move almost exactly in the plane of the planet's equator; the axial inclination of Mars is only slightly greater than that of the Earth. Because the satellites move in the equatorial plane, an observer near the Martian poles would never be able to see them.

Mars as seen from its outer satellite *right*
Mars is at half-phase, so that the large craters along the terminator are partly shadow-filled and are well seen. The south polar cap, made up either of solid carbon dioxide or a mixture of this and ordinary ice, appears to the top of the picture; the Nix Olympica, a 300-mile crater, is to the lower right. Near the edge of the 'night' half of Mars is Phobos, the inner satellite, which is much closer to Mars. The two dwarf satellites can never approach each other to within a distance of much less than 9,000 miles.

VENUS

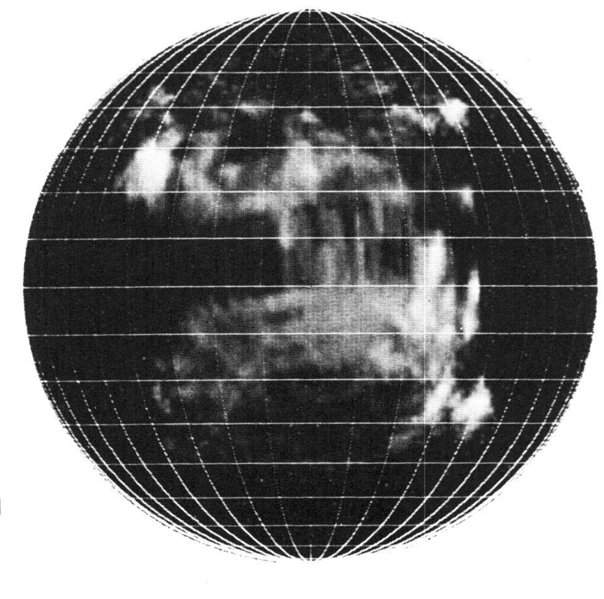

Radar chart of Venus *left*
Compiled by United States investigators. The nature of the patches is unknown, though they are undoubtedly surface features. It is possible that they are elevated plateaux. So far this is the only direct information we have of the topography of the planet.

Venus, the brilliant planet which shines so gloriously in our skies, has often been nicknamed 'the Earth's twin'. In size and mass it is strikingly similar to our world; its diameter is 7,700 miles, and its escape velocity is 6.3 miles per second. Though it is closer to the Sun (67,000,000 miles on average; its orbit is practically circular) it might be expected to have a reasonably pleasant climate.

Unfortunately this is not the case. Venus has a dense carbon dioxide atmosphere, and its surface is fiercely hot. Automatic probes have been sent there, but it is by no means certain that manned expeditions will ever be possible. Before the Space Age, Venus was regarded as potentially more welcoming than Mars, but it has proved to be a disappointment, and it has little to offer us – except in the way of scientific interest.

Through a telescope Venus shows a brilliant, almost blank disk. Few features can be seen, and those that are visible are always vague and ill-defined. The surface of the planet is permanently concealed by its dense, cloudy atmosphere, and before the age of space-probes very little was known about the surface conditions. It was thought quite likely that there might be broad oceans, containing primitive life-forms.

At its closest to us Venus can come within 25,000,000 miles of the Earth, so that it is then appreciably nearer than Mars; but it is to all intents and purposes unobservable, since it is practically between the Sun and the Earth, and its night-side is turned toward us. As the phase increases, so does the distance from Earth; and when full, Venus is almost behind the Sun. It is, in fact, a difficult object to study.

Even the rotation period was not known; the favoured value was about a terrestrial month. The one certain fact was that the atmosphere, at least in its upper layers, was very rich in carbon dioxide.

The first probe

The first successful probe to Venus – in fact, the first of all successful planetary probes – was Mariner 2. In December 1962 it passed Venus at little over 21,000 miles, and sent back the first reliable information. Much of this information was unexpected. It seems that the surface temperature was very high (several hundreds of degrees Fahrenheit) and that the rotation period was very long indeed; greater, in fact, than the planet's 'year' of 224.7 Earth-days. This slow rotation has since been confirmed by radar measurements carried out from Earth. Venus spins round in 243 Earth-days, and does so in a retrograde or east-to-west direction. This means that the length of the 'solar day' from the surface of Venus is equal to 117 Earth-days; the Sun will rise in the west and set in the east.

Subsequent radar work, carried out in America, provided the first rough map of the planet's surface. The main feature shown was a roundish patch, known provisionally as Alpha. It is about 600 miles across, and may be a mountainous area, though its exact nature is still a matter for debate.

During the 1960s several Venus probes were launched from the Soviet Union, with varying degrees of success. Finally, in December 1970, the probe Venera 7 made a controlled landing, coming down by parachute through the dense atmosphere, and transmitted from the surface for almost half an hour. It was confirmed that the surface temperature is about 890 degrees Fahrenheit, and that the atmospheric pressure is of the order of 100 times as great as that of our air at sea-level. This was in accord with the findings of the U.S. fly-by probe Mariner 5 of 1967.

To dispatch a manned expedition to a world with this sort of environment is out of the question at present, and in the foreseeable future, but research with automatic vehicles will certainly continue, if only because Venus is such a mysterious world. Exceptional precautions must be taken. For instance, there is now no doubt that at least two of the earlier Russian vehicles were put out of action during their descent through the planet's atmosphere, not because of inherent mechanical failure but because they could not withstand the extremely high temperatures and pressures. Venera 7 succeeded merely because it was tougher. Even so, it sent back signals for only a brief period and attempts will be made to land a probe which will remain in contact for longer.

One NASA proposal is illustrated in the painting opposite. It is suggested that two nuclear-powered space-ships should go from Earth to the neighbourhood of Venus, swing past the planet and go on outward to Mars; this would be a possibility in 1985. Alternatively, the gravitational pull of Venus could be used to slow down the vehicles for return to the Earth. Each probe would have extra propulsion modules attached to put them into the required trajectory, and they would return to Earth orbit for subsequent re-use. During the fly-by of Venus, the crew would make observations of the planet from a safe distance above the top of the atmosphere, and would release at least one capsule which would attempt a soft landing.

Whether the first probes of this sort will be manned is rather dubious at the moment, when it is still uncertain how astronauts will react to long journeys under reduced or zero gravity. At an earlier stage it is probable that automatic probes will be put into paths round Venus, so that they can send back data continuously during their active life.

The nature of Venus

There has been a great deal of discussion as to why Venus and the Earth are so different, but up to the present time no plausible ideas have been put forward. There seems little doubt that the answer must be connected with the lesser distance of Venus from the Sun; but how can this account for the strangely dense atmosphere, when the escape velocity is actually less than that of the Earth? We have to confess that we do not know.

More information is needed, particularly with regard to the temperature and pressure gradient in the planet's atmosphere. The only method of investigation seems to be by means of probes, such as the capsule shown at the start of its descent.

We must also reckon with the wind velocities in the lower atmosphere, which may have contributed to the failure of the early Russian Veneras. Strong winds are to be expected, and in a dense atmosphere they will have immense force – unlike the winds on Mars, which may attain velocities of over 150 knots, but which will be able to do little damage to a man-made base.

As yet it is rather difficult to forecast how quickly the investigation of Venus will be carried out. Interest in the planet has tended to wane since the discovery that it is overwhelmingly hostile, and in our list of space-targets priority has been switched to Mars – which may be unwelcoming, but is not intolerable! It is also notable that as yet (1972) no close-range photographs of Venus have been obtained. This omission will be rectified in the near future, however. A Mercury probe is planned for 1973 or 1974, and this will first by-pass Venus, using that planet's gravitational pull to swing it inward toward its main target.

In the future, it may be assumed that manned expeditions will study Venus from above its clouds, but no plans have yet been announced.

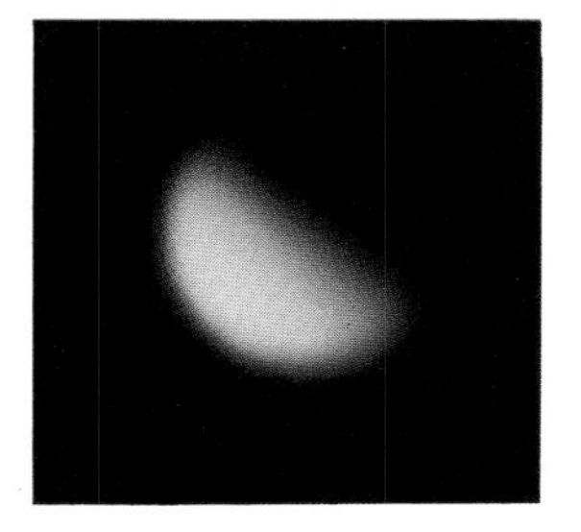

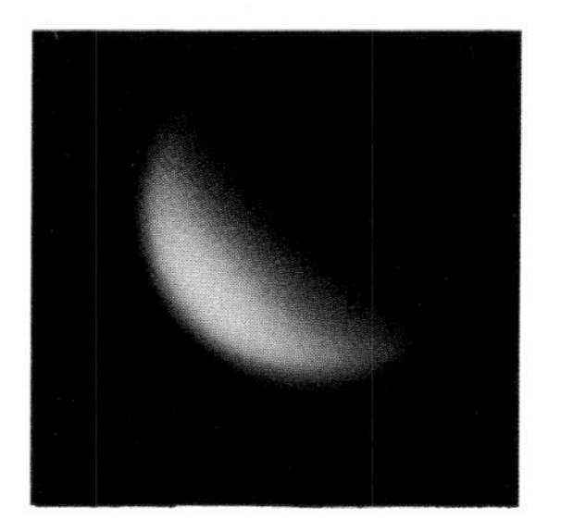

The phases of Venus *left*
Three photographs of Venus taken by H. R. Hatfield: 12-inch reflector, 1969. Note how the apparent diameter increases as the phase decreases.
Above A drawing by Patrick Moore showing the elusive Ashen Light, or luminosity of the dark side; the reason for this is still uncertain. Here it has been deliberately exaggerated.

Venus and Earth compared *above*
On this scale the difference between the two planets is inappreciable. Actually, Venus is very slightly smaller (diameter 7,700 miles as against 7,926), less dense, and less massive.

Venus fly-by probe *right*
The probes are not intended to land on the planet, and would be incapable of doing so; having swung past Venus they will continue round the Sun to Mars and return to Earth. In the painting, a capsule has just been released; this will drop through the dense atmosphere, using parachute braking, and will make a soft landing on the surface, from whence it will continue transmitting as long as possible. The main ships shown here are manned, and each carries a crew of six astronauts. In addition to making observations of Venus from close range, their programme will include studies of the space region between Venus and the Earth.

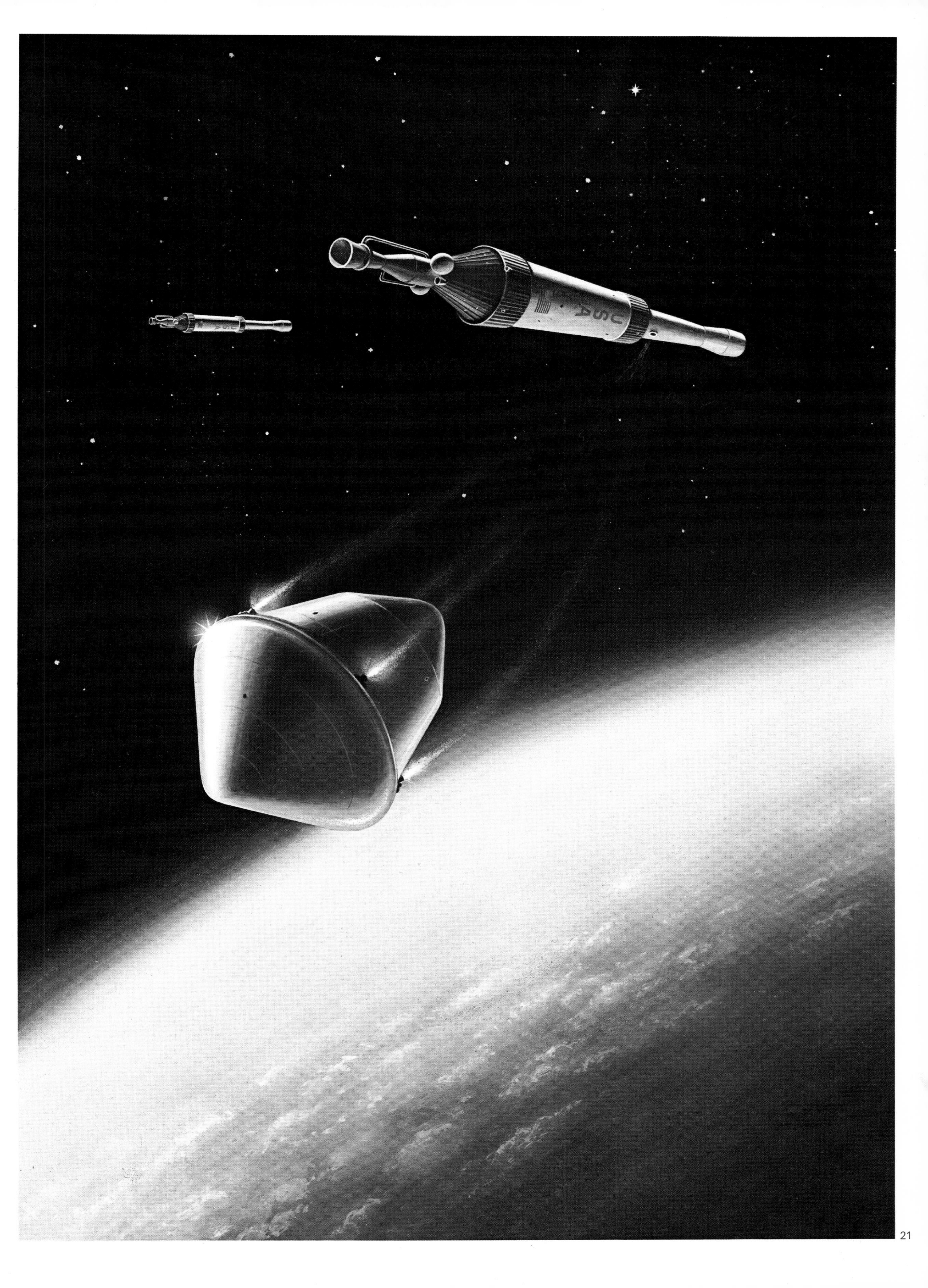
USA

VENUS 2

To the ancients, Venus was the planet of beauty; as it shines down from the twilight or the dawn sky it looks cool and peaceful. We now know that appearances are deceptive. Instead of being pleasantly cool, Venus is a Dantean inferno, and its modern nickname is 'the Hell-planet'.

The cloud-cover is complete and permanent. Some observers have suspected temporary breaks in it, but it now seems that nobody has yet glimpsed the true surface of the planet, and our only information comes from the radar measurements and, above all, from the probes which have by-passed Venus or have landed there. If Venus is photographed, in ordinary light, or in red light, no detail is seen; in blue or violet light some darker patches show up. It is logical to suppose that these phenomena are the effects of shifting cloud in the upper part of the planet's atmosphere. French astronomers have studied the movement of the clouds, and have observed a somewhat banded appearance. If the French are correct, and our radar measurements prove to miscalculations, then we shall have to revise our ideas about Venus yet again. However at the present time a majority of our astronomers believe that the rotation period is 243 Earth-days, unlike the French, who favour the theory that Venus rotates in only four days, in a retrograde direction. The shift in the features must be explained some other way. It is likely that ice crystals exist in the uppermost part of the atmosphere, but at lower levels the temperature and the pressure increase quickly, until they reach levels which would be fatal to any advanced life-forms of our own kind.

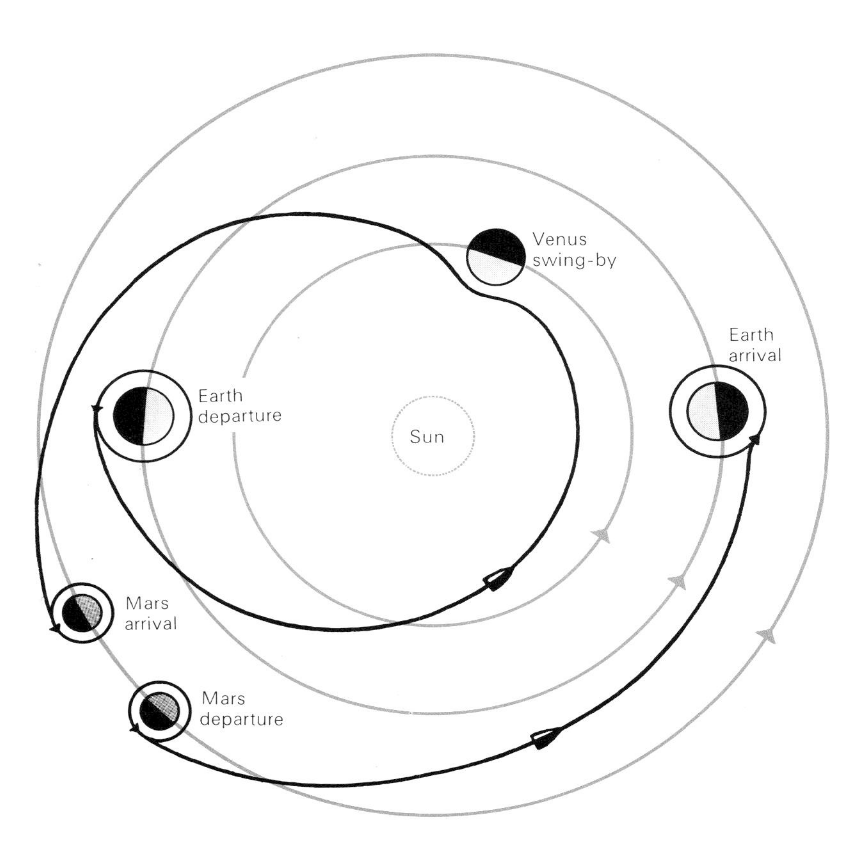

Mars via Venus *above*
An opposition-class Mars mission, including a Venus swing-by. At the moment, the projected dates for this mission are: Earth departure March 26, 1985; Venus swing-by September 12, 1985; Mars arrival March 11, 1986; Mars departure May 10, 1986; Earth arrival October 7, 1986. The projected vehicles for this project are shown in the painting on the previous page.

The atmosphere of Venus

The atmosphere of Venus is obviously extensive, and since 1932 it has been known to consist largely of carbon dioxide. However, measures from Earth, or from fly-by probes, could investigate only the upper part of the cloud-layer, and our best information comes from the Russian probes Venera 4 (1967) and Veneras 5 and 6, which landed on Venus in 1969, and entered the atmosphere at an angle of 65° to the local horizon.

The carbon dioxide produces what is known as a greenhouse effect, and traps the Sun's heat, explaining the high surface temperature of almost 900 degrees Fahrenheit. The clouds reach up as high as 35 miles, perhaps rather more, so that the total mass of Venus' atmosphere is much greater than ours.

If it were possible to go to Venus, the scene would be much as shown in the painting. The clouds would filter out most of the sunlight, leaving only a dull, reddish glow; from the surface the Sun itself could never be seen – and neither could the Earth, the other planets, or the stars. The only difference between day and night would be in the amount of illumination. Lightning would flash in the sombre, murky atmosphere, and the ground itself would be red-hot.

We do not know whether there are any mountains on Venus. Some of the patches revealed by radar, such as the 600-mile Alpha, may be elevated areas, perhaps plateaux; but any peaks would be rounded and eroded, as shown in the painting. Neither do we know whether the surface is firm or soft, and our only evidence either way is that Russia's Venera 7 transmitted for almost half an hour before contact was lost. Liquid water cannot exist on the surface of Venus, and could not do so even if conditions were favourable for it in ways other than temperature. At almost 900 degrees, water would turn into steam.

Refracted light

There is another phenomenon to be taken into account. Light-rays are bent, or refracted, when they pass into a denser medium. The lower atmosphere of Venus is so dense that it is 'super-critically refractive'. True, it is so opaque that our normal vision would be useless (an effect which has been deliberately reduced in the painting, for the sake of clarity); but even if the atmosphere were transparent, an observer would seem to be at the bottom of an immense bowl, with the horizon turning upward in every direction no matter where he stood. The effect would be weird in the extreme; and this alone would make the practical exploration of Venus very difficult.

Manned space-craft of present-day type could never go to the surface of Venus, and when we look further ahead speculation is inevitable. A capsule carrying a crew would have to be immensely durable in order to withstand the extreme temperatures and pressures, and even if it could achieve a safe landing it is not easy to see what use it would be. No astronaut would be able to venture out from the protection of the capsule. The most that could be done would be to set up recording equipment; and even this could probably be carried out equally well by an automatic vehicle.

As with Mars, so with Venus: many suggestions have been made for altering the planet's atmosphere, and making it breathable. Wild though it may sound, the idea is not so fantastic as in the case of Mars. For one thing, Venus has an escape velocity which would enable it to retain an atmosphere of terrestrial type; indeed, the trouble at the moment is that it has too much atmosphere rather than too little. Secondly, the main requirement for a breathable atmosphere is oxygen, and of this there is plenty on Venus; it is combined with carbon in the abundant carbon dioxide, CO_2.

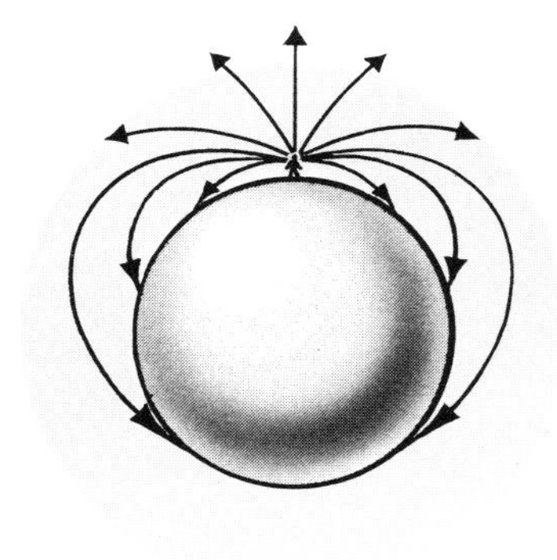

Super-critical refraction *above*
Diagram to show the effects of super-critical refraction. Because the atmosphere of Venus is so dense, it will refract light-rays very strongly, and the result will be as shown here; an observer on the planet would have the impression of being at the bottom of a huge bowl, with the horizon curving upward no matter in what direction the observer looked – assuming, of course, that it were possible to see through the dense, fuming atmosphere! Little light can reach the surface of Venus.

Suppose, then, that it were possible to 'seed' the clouds of Venus in some manner, breaking up the carbon dioxide and releasing free oxygen? On Earth, this happened early in geological history, not by artificial means but by the action of plants. The original atmosphere contained a great deal of carbon dioxide, and little free oxygen. If a present-day Earthman could enter a time-machine and go back to the Cambrian Period, more than 500 million years ago, he would choke. Then, gradually, plants spread on to the lands; and by the process of photosynthesis, these plants extracted the carbon dioxide and replaced it with free oxygen. Subsequently there arose a balance between animals, which breathe in oxygen and expel carbon dioxide, and plants, which have the reverse effect. This is why the atmosphere of the Earth remains to all intents and purposes constant in its composition.

Were Venus provided with an oxygen-rich atmosphere, and were the surface covered with plants, conditions would be tolerable so far as we are concerned. The climate would be extremely hot, because Venus is over twenty million miles closer to the Sun than Earth, but life would be possible.

As yet we have no idea whether anything of the sort could be attempted; it is well beyond the scope of our twentieth-century technology. Whether it will still be impracticable in the thirtieth century we cannot tell.

Life on Venus?

Can life of any kind exist on Venus today? In view of the hostile environment we are bound to be doubtful; but as many scientists have pointed out, life-forms of lowly kind are highly adaptable. They can survive in hot springs at a temperature not far below boiling point; and not all organisms need free oxygen. In view of this, it may be premature to say definitely that Venus is sterile, though all the evidence indicates that terrestrial-type life could never survive there. The only possibility would be life existing in the upper part of the atmosphere, where the temperatures and pressures are tolerable; but even this appears to be improbable in the highest degree.

A major step forward in our investigation of Venus would be to land a sophisticated probe there, so that signals could be received over a long period. This will certainly be attempted eventually, though the space authorities have to balance scientific advantage against the financial cost. When our techniques have advanced sufficiently we may even be able to obtain photographs from the surface, either by direct transmission or by sending a probe down through the atmosphere and then bringing it back. Strict decontamination of all samples obtained from Venus would have to be carried out, perhaps even more stringently than in the case of Mars, but the results would be of the highest interest; and it would be fascinating indeed to find out what the surface of Venus is really like.

Meantime, the painting gives an impression which is based on the best evidence available. It is only too easy to understand why we now regard Venus as 'the planet of hell' rather than 'the planet of beauty'. One day, perhaps, a human observer may be able to stand among the boiling lakes and look out into the eerie redness, punctuated by flashes of lightning; but man may never colonize Venus. Automatic probes must remain our only messengers to this strange world for many years to come.

The surface of Venus *right*
Shrouded beneath a permanent canopy of cloud through which direct sunlight cannot penetrate; the position of the Sun in the sky is betrayed only by a dull red glow. At a temperature of almost 900 degrees Fahrenheit, the surface contains lakes of tar or asphalt which boil and bubble constantly; the scene is periodically illuminated by flashes of lightning. Since the atmosphere is dense enough to cause super-critical refraction, an observer would seem to be standing at the bottom of a vast bowl, with the horizon rising up round him in every direction. Truly, Venus is a scorching inferno.

MERCURY

Mercury, the innermost planet, is a small world. Its diameter is only about 3,000 miles (slightly less, according to the latest measurements), so that it is not a great deal larger than the Moon. Its atmosphere is entirely negligible, as is only to be expected in view of its low escape velocity and its nearness to the Sun. It is much less easy to observe than Venus, since it always remains comparatively close to the Sun in the sky.

Maps of its surface have been drawn up, but are rather rough, and the chart compiled almost forty years ago by E. M. Antoniadi is still probably the best. There are darkish patches, possibly of the same nature as the waterless seas of the Moon; there may be mountains and valleys, and it is quite likely that there are craters, though we cannot see Mercury well enough to find out. We may at least be sure that no life of our kind can exist there, and the most that can be said is that Mercury, barren though it may be, may be rather less impossibly hostile than Venus.

Mercury and Earth compared *above*
Mercury (diameter 3,000 miles) is much the smaller and less massive of the two; its low escape velocity means that it has been unable to retain an atmosphere.

In the past Mercury has been a somewhat neglected planet, chiefly because it is so difficult to study, but plans have now been drawn up for the dispatch of a photographic probe to it in 1973. This will go to Mercury by way of Venus, using the gravitational pull of Venus to swing it into the correct trajectory. It will not land on Mercury, but it should obtain pictures which will be at least as good as those of Mars secured by the Mariners of 1965 and 1969.

Because Mercury is so near the Sun, it experiences great extremes of temperature. It has a rotation period of 58.5 days, and a 'year' of 88 Earth-days; to an observer on the planet the interval between one sunrise and the next would be 176 Earth-days. The hottest parts of the planet must be heated to over 700 degrees Fahrenheit, but the nights must be bitterly cold, since there is no atmosphere to waft warmth round from the day to the night hemisphere.

Mercury is an unfriendly world, but there is no reason why future expeditions should not land there, either on the night side or near sunrise or sunset – an obvious precaution in order to avoid the worst of the mid-day heat. The scene shown in the painting is probably very near the truth. A solitary plug of lava, ejected from a volcanic vent many millions of years ago and now worn down to a fraction of its original size, forms the only true landmark. The extremes of temperature have caused the surface to crumble and crack; the craters are ill-defined, with low, tumbled walls. Everything spells 'desolation'; the loneliness and the silence are absolute. In the sky, the Sun – here hidden by the rock – is terrifying; on average its disk is three times larger than as seen from Earth, and by shielding his eyes from the surrounding glare the observer would be able to see both the solar corona and the glow of the Zodiacal Light, which is caused by thinly-spread material in the main plane of the Solar System.

The Mercurian sky is black, and there is no atmosphere to hide the scene, as with Venus. The Sun will move slowly across the sky, and in somewhat erratic manner, due to Mercury's slow rotation and its variable orbital speed; its path is more eccentric than that of any other planet apart from remote Pluto.

Habitation of Mercury

We can discount any idea of life on Mercury, and neither is there the slightest prospect of making it habitable. On the other hand, a future base there is not out of the question. We are still unsure about the inclination of the axis, and it is possible that the polar zones may avoid the worst of the daytime heat. In any case it may be possible to construct bases underground. Their main value would be in studying the regions close to the Sun; undoubtedly Mercury would be a splendid observing site, if an uncomfortable and dangerous one.

Of course, this is a project for the far future; but we may expect automatic probes to land equipment on Mercury within the next decade or two. There should be no real difficulty here, at least by the standards of modern astronautics, and communications should be reliable when Mercury and the Earth are on the same side of the Sun.

The rotation of Mercury

In one important respect our ideas about Mercury have changed since the start of the Space Age. It used to be thought that Mercury's 'day' and 'year' were the same length: 88 Earth-days. Had this been the case, Mercury would have kept the same face turned permanently toward the Sun, and would behave in the same way as the Moon does with respect to the Earth. There would have been a zone of permanent day, an area of everlasting night, and an intermediate 'twilight zone', over which the Sun would have moved alternately just above and just below the horizon. It was only in the 1960s that radar measurements proved this picture to be wrong. In a way, the discovery made things more difficult. The temperatures in the so-called twilight zone would have been tolerable, with no fierce extremes of either heat or cold. Unfortunately, we now know that there is no twilight zone; every part of Mercury experiences both day and night, though the calendar is strange by our standards.

From Mercury, the view of the Solar System will be rather restricted. Like Venus, the planet has no satellite; and neither is there a planet still closer to the Sun, though a century ago astronomers believed in the existence of such a planet and even gave it a name – Vulcan. Occasional comets will come into view, their tails stretching across the blackness of the night sky; Venus will be brilliant, and the Earth-Moon system will appear as a bright double star. Yet nothing can alleviate the loneliness and the bleakness of Mercury – a world which has never known the breath of life.

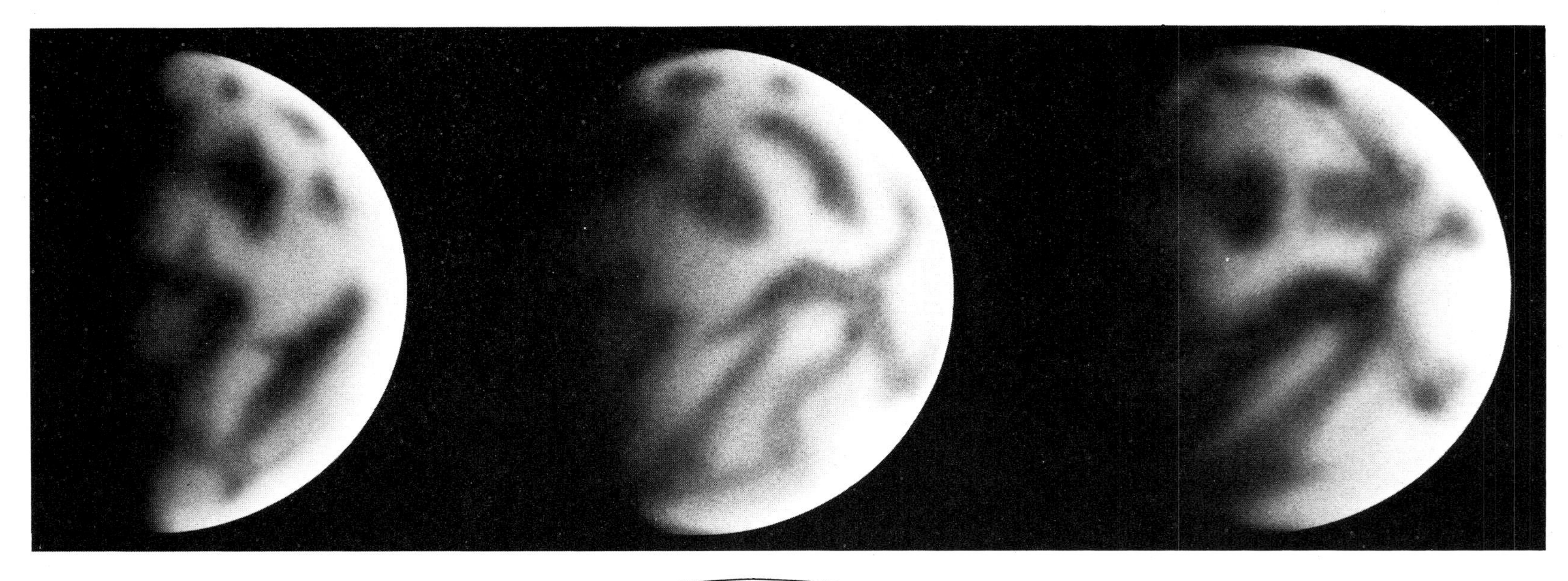

Drawing of Mercury *above*
These drawings were made by Audouin Dollfus, using the 24-inch refractor at the Pic du Midi Observatory in the French Pyrenees. The dark patches are permanent, and may be analogous to the waterless lunar *maria*.

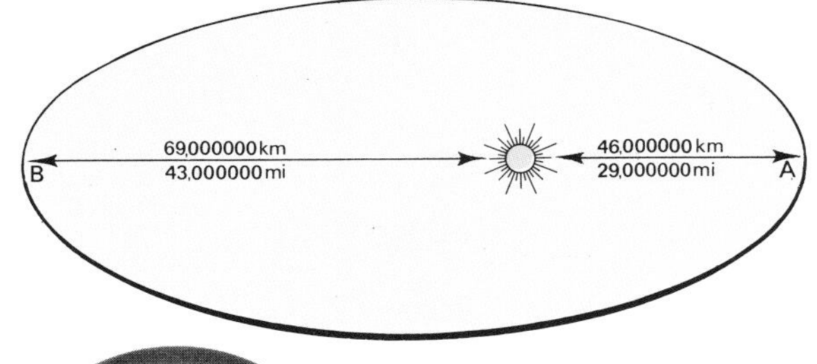

The orbit of Mercury
Above The orbit of Mercury, which is relatively eccentric; the distance from the Sun ranges between 29,000,000 miles and 43,000,000 miles. The revolution period is 88 Earth-days.

Left Because of its eccentric orbit, the Sun as seen from Mercury appears considerably larger when the planet is near perihelion. The diagram shows the Sun as seen from Mercury, to scale, at perihelion and at aphelion.

The surface of Mercury *right*
Mercury is a lifeless world of silence and desolation. The only landmark in this scene is a plug of lava, sent out by a volcanic eruption millions of years ago and since worn down by the alternate expansion and contraction of the surface materials owing to the great range of temperature between day and night; but no volcanic eruptions happen on Mercury now. Mercifully, the glaring disk of the Sun, three times the size that it appears from Earth, is hidden by the rock-column. The Earth-Moon system can be seen in the black sky, immersed in the band of the Zodiacal Light produced by debris spread in the main plane of the Solar System. From the hidden Sun, the pearly corona stretches out toward the zenith.

THE ASTEROIDS

Between the orbits of Mars and Jupiter, separating the two main groups of planets in the Solar System, we meet the swarm of dwarf worlds known as minor planets, planetoids or asteroids. Several thousands of them are known, and their total number has been estimated at anything between 44,000 and 100,000; but most of them are tiny, irregular bodies. Only three known asteroids have diameters of over 250 miles; these are Ceres (427 miles), Vesta (370) and Pallas (280). No asteroid is massive enough to retain any vestige of atmosphere.

It has been suggested that the asteroids represent the remnants of a former planet (or planets) which met with some disaster in the remote past, and disintegrated. Alternatively, it may be that the swarm was formed from material which never condensed into a planet; but all the asteroids put together would not make one body nearly so massive as our Moon.

Icarus *above*
Sweeping in from beyond the orbit of Mars, the tiny asteroid Icarus passes only 17,000,000 miles from the Sun, closer even than Mercury. As it does so, its surface is so intensely heated that it must glow red-hot.

Arthur Clarke once suggested that in its cool cone of shadow, or well dug-in beneath its surface, scientists might use Icarus to put themselves and their equipment close to the Sun, shielded by its 10,000-million ton bulk.

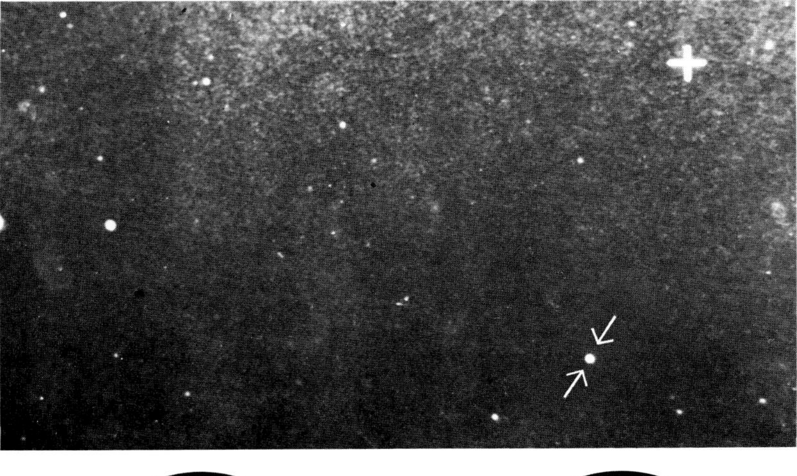

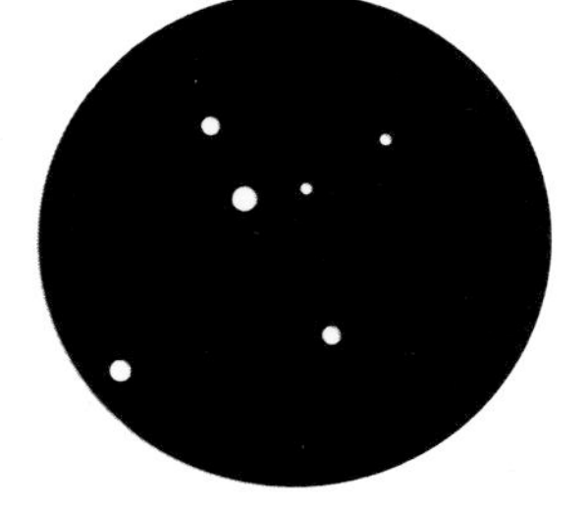

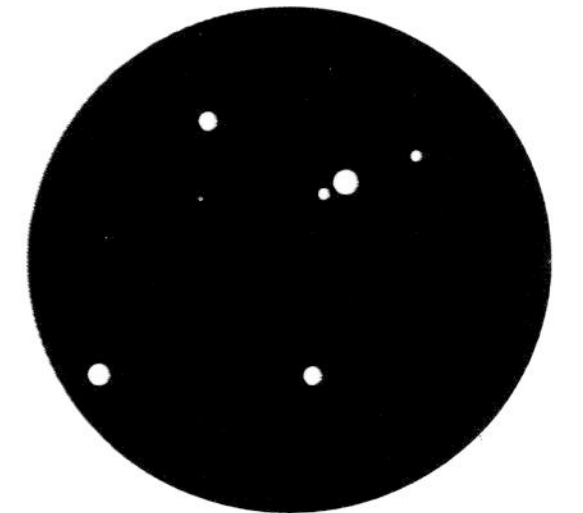

Asteroids are often regarded as rather erratic members of the Sun's family. Though they all move round the Sun in the same sense as the Earth and the main planets, some of them have orbits which are highly eccentric and inclined; Pallas, the third largest of the entire swarm, has an orbital inclination of over 34 degrees.

Though we have no information about their surface features, it is logical to suppose that the larger asteroids are at least approximately spherical. This is not true of some of the smaller members of the swarm, particularly those with exceptional orbits which swing them away from the main group and bring them relatively close to the Earth.

Eros

The first and best-known of this group is Eros, which was discovered in 1898. It has a period of $1\frac{3}{4}$ years, and its orbit swings it from just outside that of the Earth to far beyond Mars. At its nearest to us, it can come to a distance of only 15,000,000 miles – as it did in 1931, and will again do in 1975. Variations in its brightness show that it is irregular in shape, and it has even been seen elongated. Apparently Eros is shaped like a cigar 18 miles long and only about 4 wide.

Since it wanders about from the inner part of the Solar System well into the asteroid zone, Eros might be regarded as an excellent site for a 'space beacon' – and the painting shows a future scene as an expedition lands on the curious little world. Of course the small size and irregular shape produce remarkable effects of tilt; the force of gravity is negligible and, as with the satellites of Mars, touch-down will be more in the nature of a docking operation than a landing manoeuvre.

The sky as seen from an asteroid would be unfamiliar. Eros, of course, would provide great variety; when near perihelion the view would be much as seen from Earth (allowing for the lack of atmosphere), but when Eros is at its furthest from the Sun there will be many asteroids visible with the naked eye to any human observer who happens to be there. The rotation period is a mere five hours, so that the sky will spin round relatively quickly.

From a world in the thick of the main swarm, the view will be dominated by asteroids. Some of them will show visible disks, crater-pitted and irregular; others will appear as faint stars; there will be obvious movement, and the sky will be anything but static. Now and then one of the larger members will pass by, looming large for a few hours or days before receding once more; and there is always the possibility of collision.

Icarus

Of all the asteroids, perhaps the most extraordinary is Icarus. Icarus is unique in that it passes within the orbit of Mercury. At its closest to the Sun it is only 17,000,000 miles from the solar surface; at its aphelion only about 200 days later, it has moved out to a distance of 183,000,000 miles – well beyond Mars. Icarus must have the most uncomfortable climate in the Solar System.

When at its closest to the Sun, Icarus must glow a dull red as its rocks are intensely heated. Since it spins round once in every 80 minutes, the surface can hardly have time to cool before it is again bathed in the full glare of the solar radiation. In the painting Icarus is shown near perihelion; in the background the Sun blazes furiously, the pearly corona streaming out until it envelopes the wandering asteroid. The surface of Icarus is cracked and pitted, and yet only 200 days later it will be bitterly cold, with the Sun shrunken and pale in the distance.

When Icarus passes by the Earth, it might be possible to dock with it and set up an automatic transmitting station on its surface. The value of such a station could not be denied because it would provide a superb opportunity for studying the Sun from close range; but it is problematical whether any scientific instruments could survive under the conditions existing on Icarus at perihelion. The only hope would be to put them under the surface, which would reduce their value immediately. But the scene as it flew past the Sun at only 17,000,000 miles defies description; its glowing surface, the solar blaze and the contrasting blackness of the sky make up a picture which is beyond anything in our wildest dreams.

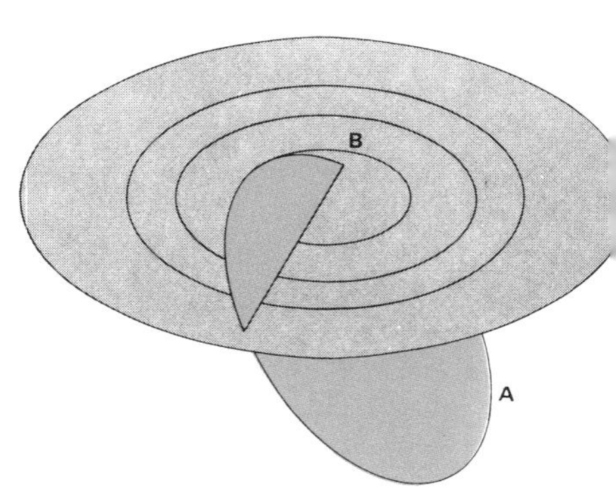

The orbit of Icarus *above*
The revolution period of Icarus is 409 days, and the distance from the Sun ranges between 183,000,000 miles at aphelion to only 17,000,000 miles at perihelion. The orbital inclination is 23 degrees. 'A' is the orbit of Icarus; 'B' that of Mercury.

The position of Vesta
Above left Vesta, brightest and second largest of the asteroids, photographed by F. J. Acfield in 1967. Vesta appears as a starlike point between the arrows. The cross above shows the position of Vesta twenty-four hours later. As will be seen, Vesta's appearance is exactly like that of a star.

Left Two sketches of the position of Vesta made by Patrick Moore in 1969. The interval is 24 hours. The stars remain in the same relative position, but Vesta has moved.

The Eros Expedition *right*
Astronauts have docked with the asteroid, and are setting up an inflatable, semi-transparent dome; they are preparing to make a geological survey of Eros itself. The asteroid is 18 miles long by 4 wide, and spins round in 5 hours. Its surface is pitted with craters, due mainly to collisions with cosmical debris in the asteroid belt; near its aphelion point Eros enters the main zone, though when at its closest to the Sun it approaches the orbit of the Earth, and may come within 15,000,000 miles of us.

JUPITER

Jupiter, innermost of the giant planets, is a world as different from Earth or Mars as it could possibly be. Its huge globe, over 88,000 miles in diameter as measured through the equator, is clearly flattened; this is due to the rapid rotation, since the Jovian 'day' is less than 10 hours long. The outer layers are made up of gas, mainly hydrogen and unprepossessing hydrogen compounds such as ammonia and methane. The internal constitution of Jupiter is not certainly known; it was once thought that there might be a rocky core, surrounded by a thick ice-layer which was in turn overlaid by the deep, hydrogen-rich 'atmosphere', but it is now thought more probable that hydrogen is the main constituent all the way through the globe, though near the centre this hydrogen is so compressed that it behaves in the manner of a metal. Undoubtedly the core temperature is high, perhaps half a million degrees, but the visible surface is very cold; it can never rise above −200 degrees Fahrenheit.

Man can never land on Jupiter. The surface is not solid, and the gravitational pull is extremely high. Fly-by probes are now fully advanced. The first Pioneer spacecraft was launched towards Jupiter early in March 1972. Eventually, landings will be made on the larger satellites of the planet.

Altogether Jupiter has twelve satellites. The outer seven are small and distant, so that they are probably captured asteroids (perhaps former members of the Trojan group). The four largest members of the family, Io, Europa, Ganymede and Callisto, were discovered soon after the invention of the telescope, and are bright enough to be seen in modern binoculars. The first two are roughly the size of our Moon, while Ganymede and Callisto are larger.

The painting on this page shows the scene from Europa, which orbits at a distance of 417,000 miles from the centre of Jupiter. The satellite has a fairly high density, but is also very reflective. It seems, therefore, that its rocky surface is overlaid with frozen gases; the surface temperature must be as low as that of Jupiter itself. There may well be craters on the landscape of Europa, but there is no atmosphere; the black sky is dominated by the immense disk of Jupiter, crossed by the famous cloud belts. Also on view is the Great Red Spot, a vividly-coloured oval patch on Jupiter, almost 30,000 miles long by 8,000 miles broad; it seems to be depressed below the general level of the clouds, and the hollow is here thrown into greater relief by the angle of illumination.

Jupiter from Europa *above*
Jupiter as seen from Europa, second of its four large satellites. We are standing near the north pole of Europa; the fore-ground is in the shadow of the hills behind us, but sunlight is striking the mountains, which are covered with 'ice' – not ordinary ice, but gases which have been frozen; the temperature is below −200 degrees Fahrenheit.

Radio emissions *below*
A speculative diagram of some of the characteristics of the radio emissions from Jupiter.
A Circular-polarized radiation
B Plane-polarized radiation
C Jupiter's rotation axis
D Jupiter's magnetic axis
E Magnetic field lines
F Paths of trapped vehicles

Amalthea

But if the view from Europa is breathtaking, the scene from the innermost of the satellites, Amalthea, is even more so. Amalthea is a small body, only about 150 miles across, and moving at 1,000 miles per minute a mere 70,000 miles above the top of the Jovian cloud-layer. From it, Jupiter fills a quarter of the sky, passing through all its phases in less than twelve hours; but any surface feature would remain visible from Amalthea for quite a long time, since the revolution period of the tiny satellite is only two hours longer than the Jovian 'day'.

If an observatory could be set up on Amalthea, endless valuable information could be obtained. The observatory shown here has been landed complete by means of a propulsion module, and the laboratories will be formed from the grounded cylindrical tank-sections.

It has been found that Jupiter is a powerful source of radio waves, and that the radio bursts are sudden and irregular. They seem to be associated with the position in orbit of Io, the innermost of the large satellites, and perhaps also with that of Amalthea. An observatory on Amalthea would lie inside the Jovian equivalent of our Van Allen radiation zone, and would lead us on to a much better understanding of the origin and the effects of planetary magnetism.

We know nothing about the surface conditions on Amalthea, since Earth-based telescopes will show it only as a speck of light (it was discovered as recently as 1892). Crater-pits are to be expected; because of the intense gravitational strain in a region so close to Jupiter, Amalthea may have been drawn out into the shape of an egg, and eventually it may even be disrupted, so that it will be spread round Jupiter in fragments to form a ring. However, this will not happen for at least 70,000,000 years; and long before then men will have gone to this curious little world.

Jupiter as seen from Amalthea *right*
The innermost satellite is only 150 miles in diameter, and possibly distorted in shape by the intensely powerful pull of gravity. Jupiter fills over a quarter of the sky; it is only 70,000 miles away, and the ever-changing atmospheric maëlstrom forms an incredible, beautiful panorama to the scientists on the observation base. The observatory is designed chiefly for studies of Jupiter itself; to the right can be seen the laboratories, formed from the cylindrical tank-sections of the propulsion module which brought the expedition to Amalthea.

SATURN

Beyond Jupiter, moving at a mean distance of 886,000,000 miles from the Sun, lies Saturn – by far the loveliest object in the entire Solar System. Like Jupiter it has a gaseous surface, and is intensely cold; like Jupiter, too, it has a satellite family, in this case made up of ten members. Saturn is smaller than Jupiter, having an equatorial diameter measured at approximately 75,000 miles.

The glory of Saturn lies in its rings, unique in our experience. The rings are composed of small particles, probably ices or at least ice-coated; they may be the remnants of a former satellite which was broken up, or they may be debris which never condensed into a satellite. The rings, as well as the inner satellites, lie in the plane of Saturn's equator.

There can be no hope of landing on Saturn, either with manned or with unpiloted vehicles. As with Jupiter, there is no solid surface. Yet we have a wealth of satellites from which to choose; and the painting shows the view which would be obtained from Rhea, the sixth satellite in order of distance from the planet.

Rhea moves at 328,000 miles from the centre of Saturn, so that in this scene the surface of the planet is less than 300,000 miles away. The beautiful ring-system is edge-on, and is visible only as a thin white line fading into darkness to the right, where the shadow of the planet falls on to it. Yet the rings make their presence known in other ways. The myriads of tiny, icy particles reflect sunlight on to the upper dark half of the planet, and a shadow is cast on to the sunlit portion.

The inner satellites

Four other satellites are visible, three of them giving the impression of pearls on a necklace since they, too, are in the same plane as the rings. The large satellite against the night side of Saturn is Dione, only 93,000 miles closer in; the

others are Tethys, Enceladus and Mimas.

Rhea itself has a diameter which may be as much as 1,000 miles. It is twice as dense as water, and the landscape shown here is basically somewhat similar to that of our Moon. In these remote depths of the Solar System there seems no reason why jagged rocks should not remain unchanged over vast periods of time; the temperature range is not great, since the cold is always so intense, and there may be fewer meteorites to pit the surface with craters. In this scene, the Sun is below the horizon, but the strong yellow light of Saturn casts a brilliant glow over the bleak, inhospitable rocks of Rhea.

Should it become possible to set up observation posts within the system of Saturn, Rhea will be a strong candidate, since it is reasonably close to the planet and yet is outside the ring-zone, where there will be a great deal of potentially dangerous debris. Rhea takes $4\frac{1}{2}$ Earth-days to complete one journey round Saturn, whereas Saturn itself spins round in only $10\frac{1}{4}$ hours, so that the panorama will be quickly-changing, and all areas of the ringed planet will come into view in relatively rapid succession.

Two aspects of Saturn
Above Saturn as seen from Rhea, the sixth satellite in order of distance from the planet. The rings appear as a thin line; the inner satellites Dione, Tethys, Enceladus and Mimas appear in the black sky. The surface of Rhea is assumed to be not unlike that of our Moon.

Left Saturn and Earth compared. Saturn has an equatorial diameter of 75,100 miles, but it is obviously flattened, and its polar diameter is less than 70,000 miles. It is, of course, a giant world, inferior only to Jupiter; but its density is very low, and is actually less than that of water. Its mass is 95 times that of the Earth, and the escape velocity is 22 miles per second.

TITAN

Of the ten satellites of Saturn, much the largest and most important is Titan, which moves round the planet at a distance of 760,000 miles (reckoned from the centre of Saturn; that is to say, rather more than 720,000 miles from the top of the cloud-layer). It has a period of 15 days $22\frac{1}{2}$ hours; its orbit is practically circular, and lies only half a degree in inclination from the plane of the rings.

Titan was discovered by the Dutch astronomer Christiaan Huygens as long ago as 1655, and is bright enough to be visible in a very small telescope. It is the densest of all the satellites of Saturn apart from Dione, and it is large. Estimates of its diameter range between 2,400 miles and 3,500 miles. Probably Titan is comparable in size with the planet Mercury, making it the largest satellite in the Solar System, though it is not so massive; it is certainly considerably larger than our Moon, and may be larger than any of the satellites of Jupiter.

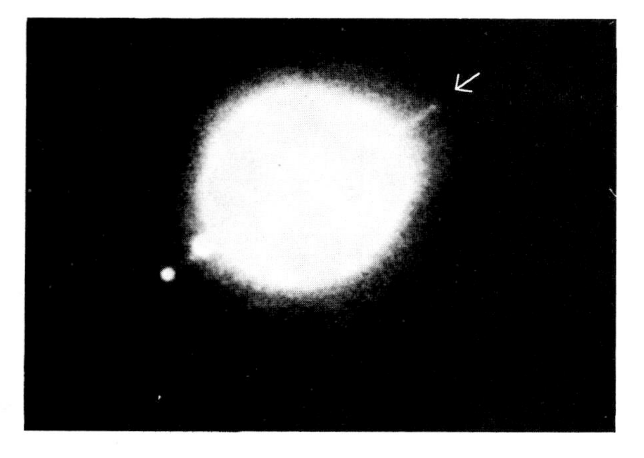

Saturn's moons
Above The inner satellites of Saturn, photographed by G. P. Kuiper: Mimas, Enceladus, Tethys, Dione and Rhea, all of which are smaller than Titan and are closer to the planet. *Left* The innermost satellite, Janus, indicated by the arrow; this was discovered by Dollfus in 1966. In both pictures Saturn itself is necessarily over-exposed.

The innermost satellites of Saturn are of very low density. Little is known about Janus, which was discovered by Audouin Dollfus in 1966. It moves not far beyond the edge of the ring-system, and is very elusive; it is observable only when the rings are edge-on to the Earth, a state of affairs which will not recur until 1980. Mimas, Enceladus and Tethys seem to have a density about equal to that of water, which, admittedly, is still greater than the mean density of Saturn itself. Dione, which may be almost 1,000 miles in diameter, is different. It is as dense as our Moon, and is presumably a body of the same type, whereas the inner members of the family have been described as cosmic snowballs. Rhea, too, is reasonably dense, and may be rocky. It is logical to assume that future bases will be set up on Rhea or Dione rather than upon the closer satellites.

Titan, with its planetary dimensions, is more than twice as dense as water, and has an escape velocity of 1.7 miles per second. So far as satellites are concerned, it is unique in that it has an appreciable atmosphere, and the effects of this are shown in the painting. Instead of being black, the sky from Titan is dark blue. The combination of this hue with the light from the pale, distant Sun and the glorious yellow Saturn-light makes a scene which is as eerie as it is glorious.

Mercury, larger and more massive than Titan and with a higher escape velocity (2.6 miles per second) is to all intents and purposes devoid of atmosphere; why, then, can Titan retain one? The reason is quite straightforward. Titan is much colder. The surface temperature can hardly be greater than that of Saturn, which has been measured at around −240 degrees Fahrenheit. Higher temperatures mean that the particles in an atmosphere move more quickly, so that they are more easily able to escape into space. This has happened with Mercury, where the daytime heat can rise to at least 700 degrees Fahrenheit; any atmosphere which may once have existed there has long since been driven off. With Titan, the situation is different. The atmospheric particles are less agitated, and have been unable to leak away. Even so, Titan represents something of a borderline case; it has been calculated that if the temperature were raised by as little as 100 degrees Fahrenheit, the atmosphere would escape.

The existence of an atmosphere was proved in 1944 by G. P. Kuiper, by spectroscopic methods. Examining the spectrum of Titan, he detected lines and bands due to methane, the poisonous gas which is often known as fire-damp or marsh gas. The density of the atmosphere is uncertain, but can hardly be very great, and there is no suggestion that an atmosphere of this sort could support life even if conditions on Titan were suitable in other ways. All the same, it is not impossible that the atmosphere may be of some use in the far future. Arthur Clarke has pointed out that methane can be used for nuclear rocket propellant, and has suggested that for this reason manned expeditions may penetrate as far as Titan before visiting the satellite system of Jupiter. Though Ganymede and Callisto, the senior members of the Jovian family, are comparable with Titan in size they do not seem to be surrounded by appreciable atmospheres. (Ganymede has an escape velocity of 1.7 miles per second; that of Callisto is decidedly lower.)

Drawings of Titan
Made by Audouin Dollfus with the 24-inch refractor at the Pic du Midi Observatory in the French Pyrenees. Light and dark areas are shown, and these are undoubtedly permanent surface features; but detail on Titan is extremely hard to make out, and can be glimpsed only with the aid of large telescopes under very favourable conditions.

Mining operations

In the painting, scientists on Titan are conducting what may be termed mining operations. An explosive equivalent to about thirty pounds of T.N.T. has just been detonated, sending up a column of material into the thin methane atmosphere. The astronauts are carrying out geological studies, and have set off the explosive to produce artificial 'earthquake-waves' in order to gain information about the depths and densities of the sub-surface rocks. Because Titan is fairly reflective, it may be coated with a layer of frozen gases. Mountains, valleys and occasional pits and craters are only to be expected.

In the sky is the crescent Saturn, its rings almost edge-on; the painting intentionally shows the rings tilted very slightly, in order to give a better impression of the effects of mutual reflection and shadow between the globe and the rings. To the left appears the crescent of Rhea, over 400,000 miles away.

Expeditions of this sort will be in the nature of reconnaissances, and it would be idle to pretend that they can be seriously planned as yet. A voyage to Saturn would take years if it were carried out by chemically-propelled vehicles. Even when nuclear rockets become operative, during the 1980s, it will be virtually impossible to reduce the time of travel to less than some months, and once again we come back to the problem of how long an astronaut can endure conditions of reduced or zero g. Yet will there ever come a time when mankind sets up a permanently-manned base in these desolate parts of the Sun's kingdom?

If the answer is 'yes', then our first remote base could well be established on Titan. The difficulties would be no greater than with the satellites of Jupiter, and the base itself would be more valuable; for one thing it could act as a relay station for more far-ranging probes, and contact with the Earth could be maintained for most of the time. During the periods when Earth and Saturn are on opposite sides of the Sun, communications would still be possible with Mars, which by then will almost certainly have full-scale colonies upon it.

From Titan the Sun seems very small. Its apparent diameter will be only 3 minutes of arc, and the amount of light and heat received will be only one-hundredth of that received on Earth. The temperature will always stay below −240 degrees Fahrenheit; in a way this will be no disadvantage, since there need be no provision against excessive daytime heat (as will be needed near the equator of our Moon).

Base on Titan

A base might well be constructed along the lines of those suitable on the Moon. Alternatively, it may be better to 'go underground', and keep only the observation rooms and the scientific equipment on the surface. Obviously there will be a need to make the colony self-supporting; to bring materials from Earth will be difficult and laborious in the extreme – and if any danger threatened the colony on Titan it would be impossible to carry out a prompt rescue operation. Neither would it be of much help to send such a rescue expedition from Mars rather than the Earth. One sometimes tends to forget the immense scale of the outer part of the Solar System; the mean distance between Mars and Saturn, for instance, is more than 740,000,000 miles.

In time it may be that all these problems will be solved. With its methane atmosphere, its dark blue sky and its icy rocks, Titan may eventually become our main outpost in the depths of the Solar System. The colonists will be scarcely able to glimpse their planet, which will be lost in the rays of the remote Sun.

Mining operations on Titan *right*
Members of an expedition to Saturn's largest satellite have just set off a powerful charge of explosive, so that shock-waves will be set up in the surface layers; these waves, measured by seismometers which have been placed at considerable distances from the explosion, will give valuable information about the composition of Titan's surface and sub-surface rocks. The rings of Saturn are seen almost edge-on; the reflection effects between globe and rings are clearly seen. The crescent of Rhea is seen to the left. Because Titan has an atmosphere, even though a tenuous one, the sky is dark blue rather than black. It is possible that Titan will be the first world in the outer part of the Solar System to be visited by man.

IAPETUS

If Titan is the most important of Saturn's family of satellites, Iapetus is the most puzzling. Its strange changes in brilliance have yet to be explained. It is also the only satellite, apart from remote Phœbe, which moves in an orbit appreciably tilted to the plane of the rings, so that from Iapetus a really superb view of Saturn will be obtained.

There is still considerable uncertainty about the origin of the rings, and indeed of the satellites themselves. All the eight inner satellites, from Janus (98,000 miles from the centre of Saturn) out to Hyperion (920,000,000 miles) revolve virtually in the ring-plane, which is also the plane of the planet's equator; this is why as seen from any of these satellites the rings will always be seen edgewise-on, and will show up as a thin line of light. The rings themselves are extremely thin. Their breadth cannot be as much as 30 miles, and may be less than 10 miles, so that when the system is edge-on to the Earth it disappears completely except in very large telescopes. But from Iapetus there is appreciable tilt, and the ring-system would be displayed to advantage, as shown in the painting.

Strictly speaking, there are three rings surrounding Saturn. Two of these are bright, and are separated by a gap known as the Cassini Division, in honour of its seventeenth-century discoverer. The Division is 1,700 miles wide, and is a genuine gap. There is no mystery about it; it is due to the gravitational effects of the inner satellites. When a ring-particle moves into the gap, it undergoes regular perturbations until it is forced into a different orbit, so that the satellites keep the Cassini Division 'swept clear'.

Between the inner bright ring and the globe is a third ring, known as the Crêpe or Dusky Ring because it is semi-transparent. A fainter dusky ring at a still lesser distance has been reported, as has another more or less transparent ring outside the main system; but these reports have yet to be confirmed.

The nature of the rings

Because the rings are highly reflective – more so than Saturn itself – they are assumed to be icy in nature, or at least ice-covered. The same may be true of the four inner satellites Janus, Mimas, Enceladus and Tethys, whose densities are about equal to that of water. It is quite logical to suppose that the rings were produced from the gravitational disruption of yet another 'ice satellite', which wandered inside the Roche limit for Saturn – that is to say, the limiting distance at which a body with no individual gravitational cohesion can exist without being broken up. The more distant satellites, Dione, Rhea, and of course Titan, are denser, and probably much more like our Moon. Little is known about Hyperion, which moves in a path beyond that of Titan; its diameter can hardly exceed 200 miles, so that in a telescope it is very faint.

Iapetus is exceptional in that it shows pronounced, regular changes in brightness. When to the west of Saturn as seen from Earth it is easily seen in a small telescope, and can become more conspicuous than any of the other satellites apart from Titan; when to the east of Saturn it fades down until it is much fainter than either Tethys or Dione. The variations are not rapid, since Iapetus is a long way from Saturn – more than two million miles – and has a revolution period of $79\frac{1}{4}$ days; but they are very noticeable indeed.

The satellite system of Saturn *below*
Of the satellites, only Iapetus and Phœbe have orbits which are appreciably tilted to the ring-plane. Phœbe, which is over 8,000,000 miles from Saturn and moves in a retrograde direction, is too distant to be shown on the same scale as the inner nine satellites.

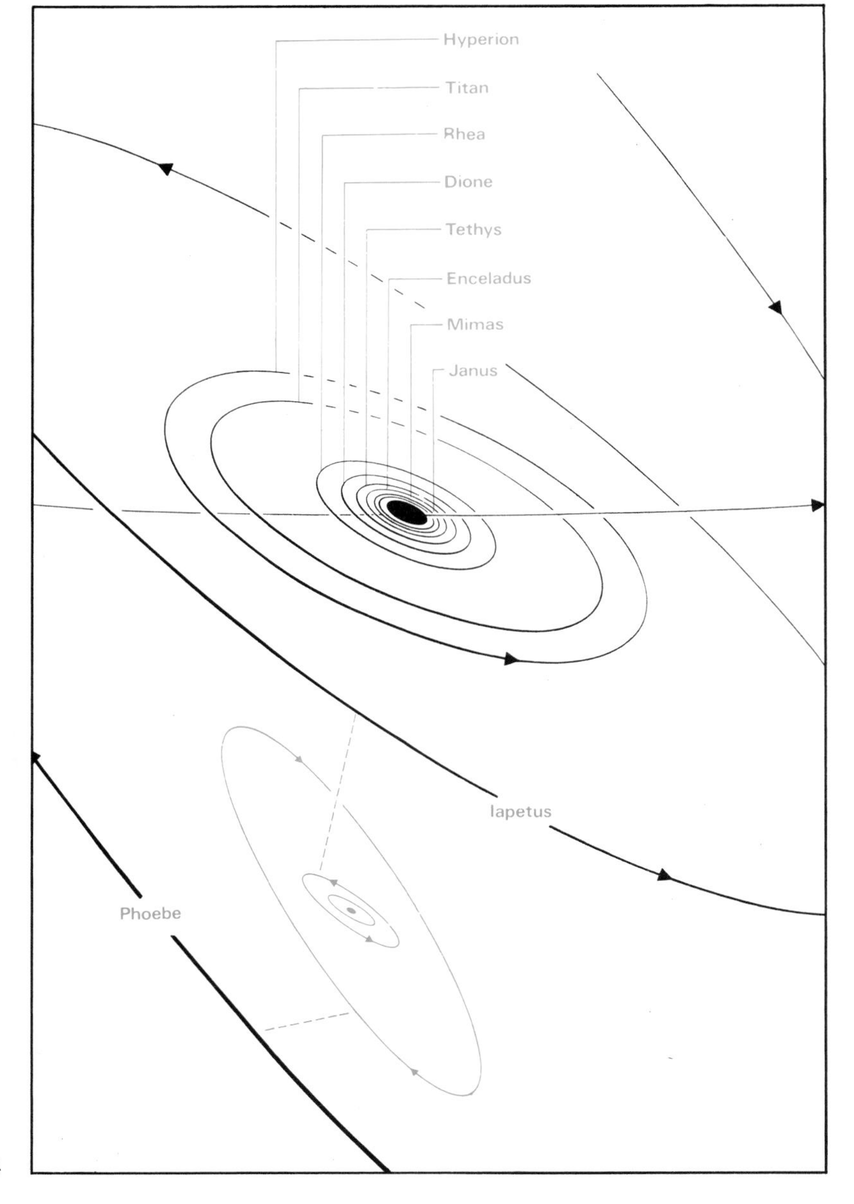

The inner satellites *above*
A photograph of the inner satellites of Saturn. Some stars are also shown in the picture. The planet itself is over-exposed, and Janus, the nearest satellite, is invisible, since it cannot be seen when the ring system is not edge-on.

Accounts of Iapetan behaviour

Various suggestions have been made to account for these changes. It may be that Iapetus is irregular in shape. Alternatively, it is possible that one hemisphere of it has been discoloured by an encounter with a wandering body in the past. Another idea is that part of the surface is ice-covered, while the remainder is bare rock; and this is the picture given in the painting, where the fringe of the ice-region is shown to the lower left.

Because the variations are regular, it seems that they must be bound up with the axial rotation of Iapetus. As we know, the Moon always keeps the same face turned to the Earth because of tidal friction over the ages. Probably the same applies to Iapetus with respect to Saturn, in which case the satellite's 'day' must be equivalent to $79\frac{1}{4}$ of ours. This would mean that from one hemisphere of Iapetus Saturn would always be visible, as shown in the painting; it would remain stationary in the black Iapetan sky, with the stars, the Sun and the other satellites drifting past it with majestic slowness. From the far side of Iapetus Saturn would never rise; and since there is no atmosphere to diffuse Saturn-light round to the opposite hemisphere, the darkness at night-time would be intense.

If Iapetus has a captured or synchronous rotation, then the same presumably applies to all the other satellites which lie closer to Saturn, since the tidal braking on them would be much greater than for Iapetus.

In a way it is unfortunate that Iapetus is over two million miles from Saturn, since it has the honour of being the only satellite from which the rings will be seen reasonably 'open' – apart from Phœbe, which is four times as remote and is very small. Phœbe may, indeed, be a captured asteroid rather than a true satellite, since it moves round Saturn in a retrograde direction, opposite to that of all the other satellites and the ring-particles; it has a revolution period of $550\frac{1}{2}$ days. From Earth it is too faint to be seen without powerful telescopes, and even from Iapetus it would appear as nothing more than a faint speck of light.

The diameter of Iapetus itself is not known with certainty, and estimates range between 700 miles and well over 1,000 miles. We cannot measure its tiny disk, and all we can do is to assume average reflecting power and work out the size theoretically. The magnitude variations make this very inconclusive, but it seems safe to say that Iapetus is smaller than our Moon.

Observatory of Saturn

From Iapetus the stars would indeed be brilliant, as the painting shows. Here Saturn lies in the head of Scorpio, the Scorpion; the bright star just above the centre of the horizon is the red giant Antares, and Delta Scorpionis lies just below Saturn to the right. Parts of the Milky Way are also visible. Of course Saturn is the dominant feature, but there will be times when it is 'new', with its night side turned toward the satellite.

Though Rhea may be a better site for studying the globe of Saturn, and Titan may be more suitable for a permanent research base, Iapetus will be pre-eminent as a location for an observatory to examine the ring system; and when men have learned how to travel out into the depths, there is every reason to suppose that an astronomical observatory will be erected on Iapetus. As with all other satellites except for Titan, there will be no glow to relieve the velvet blackness of the sky; of the other planets, only Jupiter and Uranus will be prominent, though Neptune and Pluto will be more conspicuous than from Earth.

Long before the age of manned flight out to Saturn we may solve the mystery of the fluctuations in Iapetus. Probes will by-pass Saturn, and as well as photographing the planet itself they will take pictures of the satellites – Iapetus in particular. Then we will find out for certain whether or not part of the surface is coated with bright ice. Meantime, we can only look forward to the time when human observers will be able to go to Iapetus and see for themselves the wonder and glory of Saturn's rings.

Saturn from above Iapetus *right*
Iapetus, the outermost of Saturn's large satellites; the view is taken from 200 miles above the surface. The rings of Saturn are appreciably tilted, since Iapetus has an orbital inclination of almost 15 degrees to the plane of the equator (which is also the plane of the rings). To the lower left appears the edge of a more reflective part of the surface, presumably covered with some icy substance. Saturn is almost full; the dark Cassini Division separating the two bright rings is clearly visible. In the background are the stars of Scorpio, with the red Antares particularly prominent. Iapetus has a rocky surface. The diameter of the satellite can hardly exceed 1,000 miles.

URANUS

Far beyond Saturn, moving at a mean distance of 1,783,000,000 miles from the Sun, we come to another giant planet – Uranus, just visible to the naked eye, but not known until its discovery by William Herschel in 1781. Though its diameter is less than half that of Saturn (29,300 miles) it is a world of the same basic type, and its greenish surface is gaseous, but even with a large telescope, very little surface detail is visible. Its revolution period is 84 years, and its 'day' is only $10\frac{3}{4}$ hours long. From Earth, little is visible on its pale disk, but there seem to be bright and dark zones parallel to the equator. It has five satellites: Miranda, Ariel, Umbriel, Titania and Oberon, all of which are considerably smaller than our Moon, and are consequently extremely faint.

Uranus
Above Uranus, seen from Ariel. Uranus is 119,000 miles away; the only satellite which is closer, the dwarf Miranda, appears as a crescent just above the planet. The Sun is below the horizon, to the right; its light strikes the faces of a large rock-mass. Reflected light from five fairly bright moons will render the dark portion of the planet faintly visible to eyes adjusted to the conditions, and atmospheric bands are shown.

Right Uranus and Earth compared. Uranus has 47 times the volume of the Earth, but the surface gravity is only slightly greater.

Far right The curious axial tilt of Uranus, which amounts to 98 degrees. Sometimes a pole faces the Sun, while at other times the equator is presented.

The strangest thing about Uranus is the tilt of its axis. The tilt is 98 degrees – and since this is more than a right angle, the rotation is technically retrograde. This means that the 'seasons' are peculiar in the extreme. First much of the northern hemisphere, then much of the southern will be in darkness for 21 Earth-years at a time, with a corresponding midnight sun in the opposite hemisphere, though for the rest of the Uranian 'year' there will be a more regular alternation of day and night.

This curious tilt will show up to advantage when we can observe Uranus from its satellites, all of which move in the plane of the equator – and this is the scene shown in the painting, in which Uranus is seen from its innermost large satellite, Ariel. We observe a phenomenon which cannot be seen from any other satellite system: a crescent planet, the horns of which extend not from pole to pole but almost from one side of the equator to the other. The bright equatorial band will always lie directly across the centre of the globe, but the planet will not show what we may call 'normal' phases. At the present time (1972) it will wax and wane between gibbous and crescent, but will never be full; by 1985, (by which time a probe should have reached Uranus), one pole will face the Sun, and the satellites will see a half-planet from any point in their orbits – the terminator lying at an angle of 8 degrees across the equator. The reason for this remarkable tilt of Uranus is not known; and neither is it shared by any other planet in the Sun's family.

From the satellites, the changing details on Uranus will be splendidly displayed, though the surface seems to be less active and multi-coloured than that of Jupiter or Saturn.

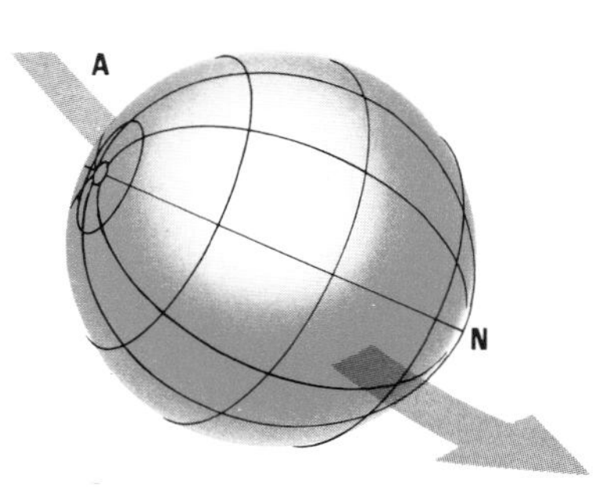

NEPTUNE

Neptune, moving at an average of 2,793,000,000 miles from the Sun, is the outermost of the giant planets. In fact, at the present time it marks the frontier of the planetary system; Pluto, which can recede to a much greater distance, is coming in toward its perihelion, and from now until beyond the end of the century it will be actually closer to us than Neptune.

Neptune was discovered in 1846. It is too faint to be seen with the naked eye, but binoculars will show it as a starlike point; it is rather bluish in colour, and it does not share the extreme axial tilt of Uranus. It is slightly larger and more massive than Uranus, but in constitution the two must be very alike.

At its great distance from the Sun and from the Earth, Neptune appears small and faint to us, and surface details are very hard to make out, though there is evidence of the familiar bright and dark zones. The atmosphere consists largely of methane; at the very low temperature (around −360 degrees Fahrenheit) the ammonia is frozen out. Methane is a strong absorber of red and yellow light, which accounts for the blue colour of the disk and the darkening of the limb shown in the painting – which depicts Neptune from its major satellite, Triton.

Triton is one of the largest satellites in the Solar System, and according to some estimates its diameter may be as much as 3,000 miles. In any case, Triton is larger than the Moon, and comparable with Mercury. As it also seems to be quite dense, with a reasonably high escape velocity, it would be expected to have an atmosphere, though up to now this has not been detected; we must assume that the Tritonian sky is black.

Triton moves at less than 200,000 miles from the cloud-layer of Neptune – closer than the distance between the Moon and the surface of the Earth. It has a revolution period of $5\frac{3}{4}$ days, but it

travels in an east to west or retrograde direction, opposite to that in which Neptune spins on its axis. Therefore the change of view will be rapid, and the features will seem to shift quickly, as the planet itself has a reasonably fast rotation (around 14 hours).

Sunlight reaching Neptune is relatively feeble, but the human eye adapts itself readily, so that the sharp sunlight glancing over the peaks (from 'behind', and slightly to the right of the observer) seems bright in comparison with the soft, diffused radiance from Neptune itself. The high inclination of Triton's orbit (160 degrees), combined with the planet's own normal-type axial inclination (29 degrees) takes Triton high over Neptune's northern hemisphere.

The other satellite of Neptune, Nereid, is extremely small; its diameter is less than 200 miles. It has a remarkably eccentric orbit, so that its distance from Neptune ranges between 867,000 miles and over 6,000,000 miles. It is therefore always much more remote from the planet than Triton, and it offers few advantages as an observation base. Eventually, however, an outpost may well be erected on Triton.

Neptune
Above Neptune as it appears from its major satellite, Triton. In the absence of atmosphere the sky will be black, and will be dominated by the bluish globe of Neptune, which will seem to spin quickly – partly because it really has a rapid rotation, and partly because Triton is moving round the planet in a retrograde direction. The stars will be brilliant, but the Sun will be comparatively small and feeble, and none of the other planets will be brilliant. This applies even to Uranus.

Left Neptune and Earth compared. Neptune is slightly larger than Uranus, with a diameter of 31,500 miles according to a recent, improved estimate. The surface gravity 1.2 times that of the Earth.

PLUTO

Toward the end of the last century Percival Lowell, well known for his theories of the Martian canals, studied the movements of the outermost giant planets Uranus and Neptune, and came to the conclusion that they were being perturbed by a more distant planet which had yet to be discovered. He instituted a search at Flagstaff, where he had set up an important observatory, but without success. It was only in 1930 that the planet was found. The discoverer was Clyde Tombaugh, working at the Lowell Observatory; and the planet was almost exactly where Lowell had said it would be. It was named Pluto. Since then, it has set astronomers one problem after another!

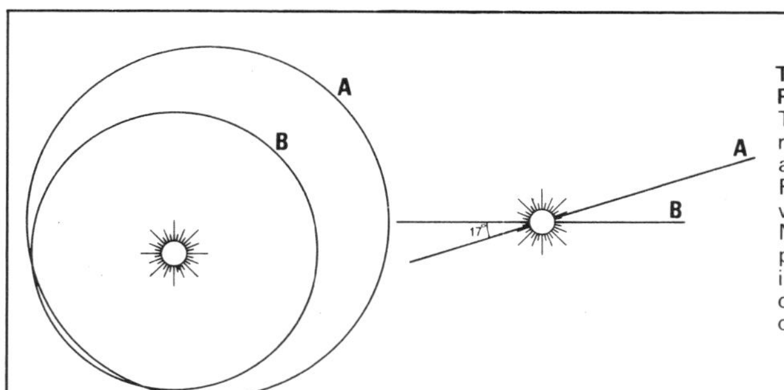

The orbit of Pluto
The eccentricity is relatively high, and at perihelion Pluto comes within the orbit of Neptune; perihelion is due in 1989. (A) Orbit of Pluto. (B) Orbit of Neptune.

Pluto is usually termed 'the frontier planet', but at present this is not true. Its mean distance from the Sun is much greater than that of Neptune, and it has a revolution period of $248\frac{1}{2}$ years; but it is approaching perihelion, which will be reached in 1989 – and its orbit is relatively eccentric, so that for the next few decades it will be closer in than Neptune can ever come. However, there is no danger of a collision. Pluto's path is inclined at the relatively high angle of 17 degrees, and it cannot have even a moderately close encounter with Neptune.

Pluto escaped Lowell's personal search because it was much fainter than had been expected. Even now, when it is nearing its point of closest approach, it cannot be seen with a small telescope; and even large instruments will show it as nothing more than a dot of light. Its diameter is therefore very hard to measure, but at an early stage it was found to be small. Instead of being a giant, such as Neptune or Uranus, it proved to be smaller than the Earth, and probably smaller than Mars. The most recent estimate of its diameter yields a value of 3,700 miles. Of all the principal planets, only Mercury is smaller.

This presents an immediate problem. If Pluto is small, and of average density (say 5 times that of water), it must be of slight mass; it can certainly not produce observable effects upon the movements of giants such as Uranus. But it was by these very effects that Pluto was tracked down!

The discovery of Pluto *above*
Photographs were taken at the Lowell Observatory (Flagstaff, Arizona) by Clyde Tombaugh during his search for the planet which Lowell had predicted. The bright, very over-exposed star is Delta Geminorum, of the third magnitude. The first photograph was taken on March 2, 1930; the second on March 5. In the interval, Pluto – indicated by the arrows – had moved perceptibly, and by just the expected amount. Within a few days Tombaugh announced his discovery.

Various efforts have been made to account for this curious state of affairs. It was even suggested that Pluto might be exceptionally dense; but with a diameter of less than 4,000 miles, the required density works out at much greater than that of iron, which seems unreasonable. Alternatively, A. C. D. Crommelin proposed that Pluto is really larger than we suppose, and that what we are measuring is not the full diameter of the planet but merely a bright area reflecting the image of the Sun. This 'specular reflection' theory is not out of the question, but there are doubts as to whether Pluto can have a shiny surface; more probably the albedo or reflecting power is low.

A third theory is that Pluto is not the planet for which Lowell was looking, and that the real perturbing body remains to be found. This, too, is a possibility; but the chances of locating a planet more remote and fainter than Pluto are not very high, since nothing is known about its position. Of course, we may always suppose that Tombaugh's discovery was due to sheer luck – but this would indeed be a remarkable coincidence. At present the puzzle of Pluto remains unsolved.

One trouble is that we have no reliable information about its mass; it has no satellite, at least so far as we can tell. However, its diameter is not much greater than that of Triton, if the latest measurements are accepted, and it may be that Pluto is nothing more nor less than an ex-satellite of Neptune which broke free and moved away in an independent orbit. Support for this idea is provided by the fact that Triton, alone of the large satellites in the Solar System, moves round its primary in a retrograde sense. This may have been the result of major disturbances, due perhaps to a wandering body, which allowed Pluto to leave the Neptunian system.

Pluto's light

Pluto's light is not quite steady. There are regular variations, and these seem certainly to be due to axial rotation. It is thought that the Plutonian 'day' is equal to 6 Earth-days and 9 hours. Since not even the world's largest telescope will show a perceptible disk, nothing is known of the surface features; but when Pluto is at aphelion, well over 4,000 million miles from the Sun, the temperature must be very low indeed even when compared with the −360 degrees Fahrenheit of Neptune.

Even though the escape velocity of Pluto must exceed 2 miles per second, it cannot possess an atmosphere at all similar to ours – for the simple reason that such an atmosphere would freeze. If Pluto ever possessed an atmosphere of terrestrial type, it would now lie frozen or liquefied on its surface rocks; and this is the theme of the painting, which shows the view from a cave-opening on Pluto.

We are looking out across a sea – not of water, but of liquid methane. The icicle-like structures from the roof of the cave are unchanging; on Pluto there is no movement, no sound, no life – nothing but the most utter silence and desolation. In the distance, the Sun appears as an intensely bright point, but little more; its apparent diameter is about the same as that of Jupiter as seen from Earth, though on Pluto it would still cast more light than our full moon. Stars can be seen, but there are no bright planets. From Pluto, only Neptune would appear more conspicuous than as seen from Earth, and even Neptune would be out of view for long periods.

Travel to Pluto

Long before manned craft can venture out into these depths, we ought to have close-range photographs of Pluto. These could be secured from the Grand Tour probes which might be launched within the next ten years. It will be fascinating indeed to find out whether Pluto is really covered with methane oceans, and whether its surface is mountainous and rugged or smooth and reflective.

It is even possible that interplanetary probes might lead on to the detection of the trans-Plutonian planet, if it exists. After having by-passed Pluto, the probe should still maintain radio contact with Earth, so that its position will be known. If it is perturbed from its calculated path, the cause might be tracked down to a new planet – and once we have any clue as to the position of the hypothetical planet among the stars, a serious search can be put under way with a giant telescope.

It is much too early to speculate as to the possibilities of establishing a base on Pluto; questions of this sort may belong not to the twenty-first or twenty-second centuries, but more plausibly to the thirty-first or thirty-second. Yet if an automatic station could be set up there the scientific information drawn from it would be of the greatest value, and there is no reason why this should not be done in the foreseeable future.

Communication with Pluto

There will be many problems to be solved, notably those of guidance and control; remember that even when an order is transmitted, it cannot be acted upon for over five hours, since it takes that time for the signal to reach the neighbourhood of Pluto. Any soft landing will have to be purely automatic, and will depend upon radar controls carried in the probe itself – as has actually been carried out already, by the Russians, with their soft-landing probes on Venus. No 'last-minute' corrections will be possible, and if anything goes wrong with the instrumentation the controllers from Earth will be helpless. Nonetheless, putting an automatic transmitting station on Pluto seems much less far-fetched now than putting a man on the Moon did at the end of the last war.

From Pluto, an observer – human or mechanical – would have admittedly a poor view of the planetary system, but there would be advantages in studying the Sun from a great distance, since very slight changes in overall brightness would be much easier to detect. Also, it is important to find out more about the amount of meteoric matter and cosmical debris in these far-away regions; and from Pluto studies could be made of those erratic wanderers, the comets, which must by-pass Pluto's orbit on their way inward to the neighbourhood of the Sun and the Earth.

Beyond Neptune and Pluto we come to a vast gulf. Even the nearest star is more than 4 light-years away, and as seen from Pluto the starry sky would look the same as it does from Earth – allowing for the lack of atmosphere. Outward, then, we look into the lonely emptiness of the Galaxy. Pluto is a world of isolation; in our painting, it is only necessary to look out from the cave-mouth at the tiny point which we know to be our splendid, blazing Sun. No lunar landscape, no Martian desert can compare with the terrifying solitude of Pluto.

The bleak landscape of Pluto *right*
Pluto is not a gas-giant, similar to Uranus or Neptune, but a small body, with a diameter less than that of the Earth or Mars. If it ever had an atmosphere, this must now lie frozen on the surface rocks, or perhaps liquefied; the painting shows waveless lakes of liquid methane. Looking out from the mouth of the cave into the black sky we see the tiny Sun, still intensely brilliant, but too small to appear as anything but a speck with the naked eye. Beyond Pluto there is nothing but emptiness – until we come to the stars, millions of millions of miles away. Of all the worlds in the Solar System, Pluto must surely be the most inaccessible.

THE GRAND TOUR

With present-day rockets, a journey to the depths of the Solar System would take decades. But conditions at the end of the 1970s are not quite normal. The outer planets are arranged in such a way that we can plan a strange, highly ambitious programme – that of the Grand Tour. Basically, this involves using the gravitational field of one planet to swing the probe outward toward its next target.

Several versions of the Grand Tour are possible, but it will suffice to describe one in detail. It would begin in 1977, the unmanned vehicle being put into a path which will carry it out toward Jupiter. It would not, of course, approach the Giant Planet too closely; it would swing round, having picked up extra acceleration on approach. It would then be directed outward toward Saturn, and the process repeated; this time the orbit would take the probe out to Pluto.

It is coincidence that conditions are suitable just at the time when our technology has advanced sufficiently for us to utilize it. If the opportunity is lost, it will not recur for over a century. This is not to suggest that the outer planets cannot be reached before then; but it will take longer, since the 'Grand Tour' technique cannot be used.

Though the Grand Tour is straightforward in principle, it is extremely difficult to put into practice. One disadvantage is that there is no time for rehearsal. The Tour probes must be launched on schedule, and even with their reduced time-scale they would still take years to reach their targets.

At present, the two most useful programmes would begin in 1977 and 1979 respectively. The 1977 probe would by-pass Jupiter in 1979, Saturn in 1980 and Pluto in 1985. The second probe, beginning its journey in 1979, would reach Jupiter in 1981, Uranus in 1985 and Neptune in 1988. Modifications to the scheme may be introduced before the time for launching draws near, but in any event Jupiter, with its immensely powerful gravitational field, is the key to the whole situation.

These two Tours are shown in the diagram below – which, for the sake of clarity, has not been drawn to an exact scale, and does not show the orbits of the inner planets.

The main problems

The problems to be solved fall into two distinct categories. First, of course, the probes must be put into the correct orbits, and contact with them must be maintained. Special computers are being designed to be taken in the vehicles – and it is hoped to make these so sophisticated that they would be able to locate and cure any faults in them which may develop.

The second problem is that of getting the information back from the probes. The difficulties become greater with increased distance, as has been found even in our own part of the Solar System. Communications with men on the Moon are easy; direct speech is perfectly clear, and the television pictures are as sharp as those from an ordinary transmitting station on Earth. Yet to receive the Mariner pictures of Mars takes a long time – and inevitably the clarity suffers.

The American authorities are confident that these problems could be solved in good time, and, were the Tours to go ahead, they would expect to receive pictures of worlds such as Uranus which would be as good as those obtained of Mars by Mariner 4 in 1965. This would be a triumph indeed, but it could be accomplished.

The view of Jupiter given here is a representation of the type of picture to be expected from the Pioneer probe launched in March 1972 and the next, due in April 1973. The probe is assumed to be some 100,000 miles from the planet. It has passed Jupiter, which has become a crescent. The usual scan-lines and blemishes have been added to the picture, which therefore may be said to be a 'preview' of what would actually be shown on television screens in 1974.

From Jupiter, a Grand Tour probe would pass on to Saturn – its trajectory taking it under the planet, so as to be clear of ring-particles and the major satellites. (Iapetus is the only large satellite with an orbit appreciably inclined to the ring-plane, and even here the tilt is only about 15 degrees.) In 1980, at the time when the probe should reach Saturn, the ring-system will be edge-on to both the Sun and the Earth; the rings are therefore shown illuminated only by light reflected from the globe of Saturn and by the slight amount by which sunlight diffuses through the rings. Despite this, special equipment may be used to find out, once and for all, how many divisions there are in the ring-system. Cassini's is the only real division whose existence has been conclusively proved as yet, though several others have been suspected. We should also learn whether or not the two extra dusky rings, one inside the main system and the other beyond, have any real existence.

After Saturn

After its dive to the south of Saturn the probe would sweep out at a sharp angle to the ecliptic to continue on to Pluto, by-passing the planet in 1985. This is four years before Pluto reaches perihelion, so at this time the distance from the Sun will be less than that of Neptune. The movements of the probe would tell us how massive Pluto is – and this is something that astronomers very much want to know; it will enable them to decide whether Pluto is or is not a bona-fide planet. If pictures of the surface can be obtained, they will be the most amazing photographs ever taken. They may even show the weird, dimly-lit lakes of liquid methane which may possibly exist on Pluto.

After passing Pluto, the probe would continue in its orbit round the Sun, since it would not be travelling fast enough to break free from the solar gravity and

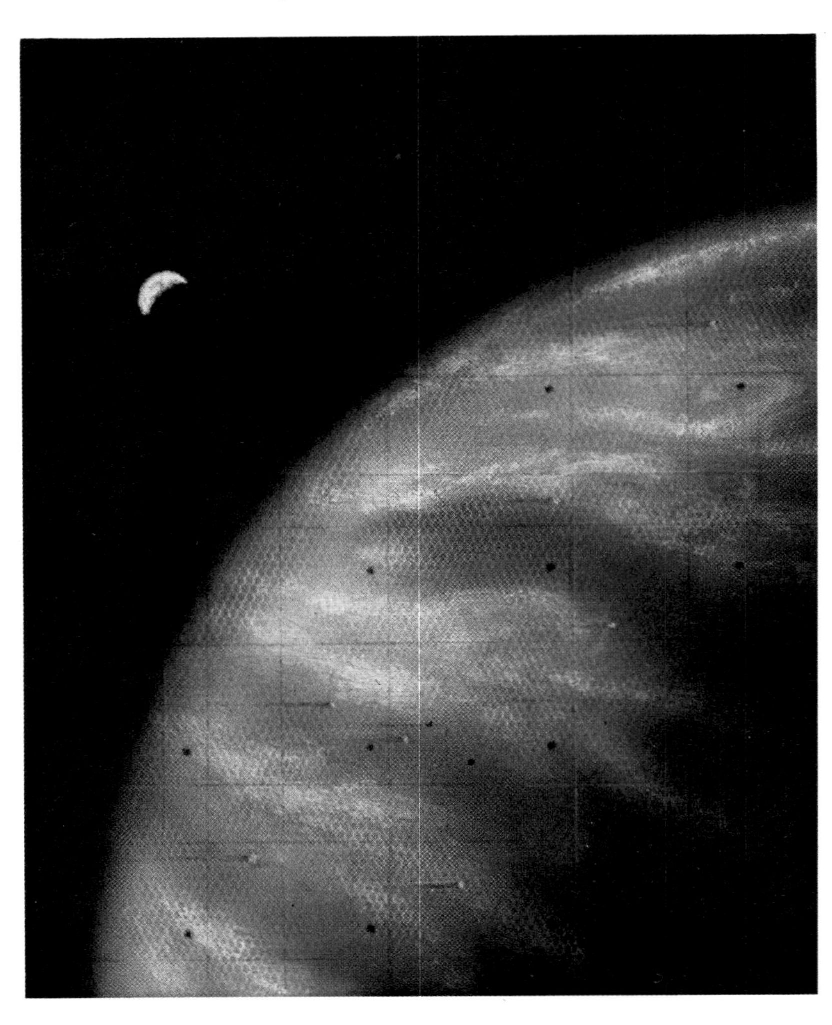

'Mock-up' photograph *above*
We may hope to receive photographs from a Pioneer probe some 100,000 miles from Jupiter, assuming that the picture quality will be at least equal to that of Mariner 4 (1965) and perhaps equal to Mariners 6 and 7 (1969). The usual scan-lines and imperfections have been added to the picture, making it completely realistic. Jupiter appears as a crescent, as does the satellite Io; this shows that the probe has passed the planet.

Two possible Grand Tours *below*
The first probe, to be launched in 1977, would go to Jupiter, Saturn and Pluto. The second would begin its flight in 1979, and by-pass Jupiter, Uranus and Neptune. For clarity, the diagram is not to scale.

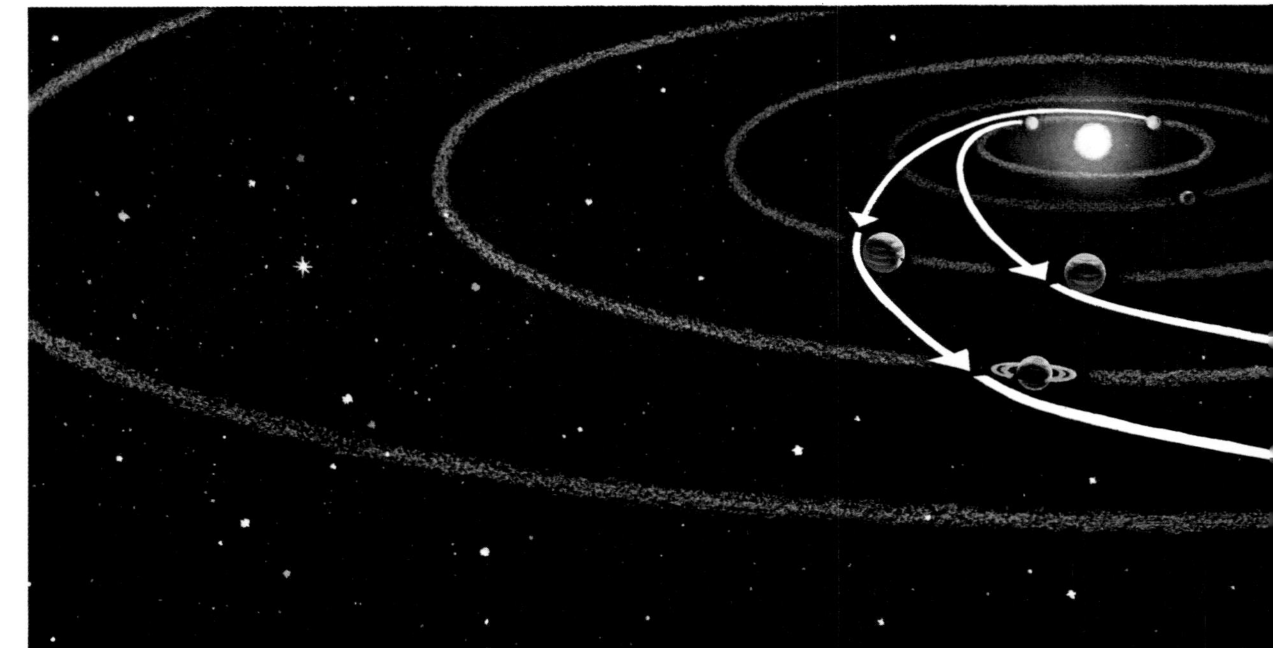

escape from our System. It would follow an elliptical path, and would become a permanent member of the Sun's family. It would not return to Earth, but we might hope to keep in touch with it for a long time, even though its power must fail eventually.

Experience gained with this first probe would be of great use in preparing the second, scheduled to be launched two years later, at about the same time that its forerunner reaches the region of Jupiter. The second probe would also by-pass Jupiter, but its trajectory would then swing it on not to Saturn, but to Uranus. This planet would be reached in 1985; by then the probe would be so distant that its signals would take $2\frac{3}{4}$ hours to reach us. One pole of Uranus would face the Sun, while the other is having its immensely long period of night. In the painting the probe is approaching over the sunlit side of Uranus.

The last target would be Neptune – at this period the outermost planet. Then the probe, like the first, would continue in an elliptical orbit round the Sun, continuing to send back data until contact with it is lost.

The Grand Tour nears Saturn *above*
The time is 1980; the rings are seen edgewise-on to the Sun and to the Earth, so that they are only dimly illuminated. The Cassini Division can be seen, and there are indications of other divisions in the bright rings; exactly how many divisions exist is still a matter for debate. The Crêpe Ring, which lies between the bright rings and the globe, is not visible under these conditions. On the planet itself, the various cloud belts and bright zones are shown; near the top the shadow of the ring crosses the disk. The probe has been directed in a way that keeps it clear of the ring-plane; otherwise it would be in danger of colliding with debris, and we do not know how far from Saturn this layer of thinly-spread debris may extend.

Cost of the Grand Tour

A Grand Tour probe would cost much less than an Apollo mission, but finance is very much to be considered in drawing up the plans, and in January 1972 President Nixon shelved the American Grand Tour plans for just this reason. If it were possible to use the most powerful rocket launchers available, and to equip the Tour vehicles without economizing, it would be practicable to take small descent vehicles and detach them at the appropriate moments, so that they could make landings on either the giant planets or their satellites. Naturally, a descent vehicle could not survive impact on Jupiter or any other giant; but the information drawn from it during the near-approach would be invaluable. Whether this project will be attempted or not remains to be seen. Moreover, it is reasonable to assume that Grand Tour journeys will be attempted by the Russians, and the financial restrictions here are likely to be less stringent.

The lining-up of the outer planets will last for some time – quite long enough for several Tour probes to be sent up. With the rapid rate of present technological progress, there is no reason to suppose that at least some of the vehicles will not be successful; and if we can indeed obtain information from these cold, remote parts of the Solar System, we will be entitled to say that the Grand Tours will make a fitting climax to the 1970s.

The probe approaching Uranus *above*
At about the time that the first Grand Tour probe is by-passing Pluto, the second should reach the neighbourhood of Uranus, and give us our first close-range view of this strange, greenish giant. In the painting, the probe is approaching over the sunlit hemisphere of Uranus; the pole is turned sunward, and on the opposite hemisphere there is a period of darkness lasting for approximately 21 Earth-years. As with Saturn, cloudy belts and brighter zones are visible. If the equipment on the probe is functioning well, we may also obtain pictures of the satellites of Uranus, all of which are smaller than our Moon. These satellites revolve in the plane of the equator, and are not shown in the painting.

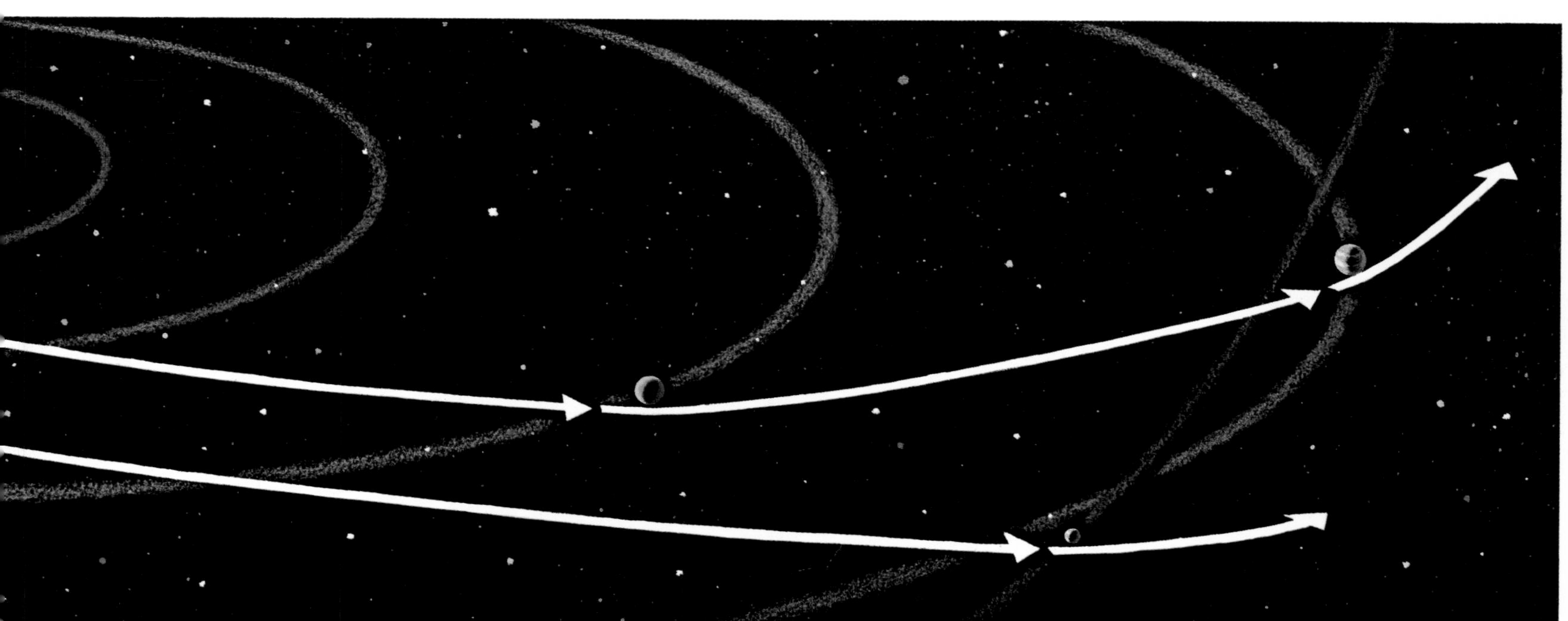

COMETS

Comets are the erratic wanderers of the Solar System. Unlike planets they are not solid, massive bodies; they are composed of relatively small particles, mainly icy in nature, together with extremely tenuous gas. Compared with a planet, the mass of a comet is negligible, even though some great comets of the past – such as that of 1843 – have been larger than the Sun. Due to the effects of solar wind (streams of electrified particles coming from the Sun), the tail of a comet always points away from the Sun, so that a comet which is moving outward travels tail-first.

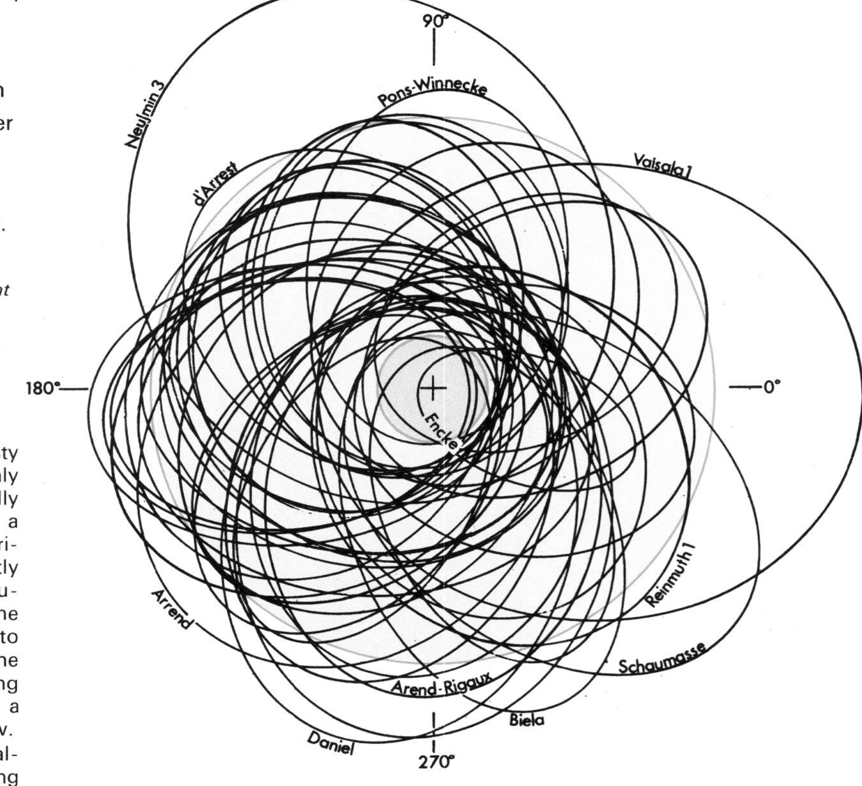

Orbits of the short-period comets *right*
Classed as belonging to Jupiter's 'comet family'. It used to be thought that comets came from outer space, and were captured by the pulls of the planets, so that they were forced into elliptical orbits, but this theory is no longer accepted.

The idea of sending a rocket probe to a comet is not nearly so far-fetched as might be thought. Indeed, the attempt may be made in the relatively near future. The only part of a comet which is of appreciable mass is the nucleus, and even this is only a few miles in diameter at most. Consequently, a probe could pass right through the head or tail of a comet without being harmed – though there is, of course, always the risk of collision with a cometary particle large enough to cause serious damage, and close-range investigations of comets will certainly be restricted to unmanned vehicles only!

Types of comet

Comets are of two main kinds. First there are the so-called short-period comets, which move round the Sun in periods of a few years; Encke's Comet, for instance, returns to perihelion every 3.3 years. Almost all these comets have very eccentric orbits, and since a comet depends upon sunlight we can observe it only when it is comparatively close to the Sun and to the Earth. Most of a comet's light is reflected, though when near perihelion the action of the Sun causes the materials in the comet to emit some light on their own account.

The short-period comets are too faint to be visible with the naked eye. Quite often it is found that the aphelion point is close to the orbit of Jupiter and it is permissible to speak of Jupiter's 'comet family'. One such comet is d'Arrest's, which has a period of 6.7 years and is due at perihelion once more in 1976. It has been under observation regularly ever since its discovery by H. d'Arrest in 1851, and its orbit is very well known. To send a probe to it, passing through the head and making measurements of the particle density – perhaps even photographing the nucleus – seems to be practicable.

Many of the short-period comets have no tails, and appear as dim, misty patches without structure. The only periodical comet which becomes really spectacular is Halley's, which has a period of 76 years; it last came to perihelion in 1910, and we may confidently expect it once more in 1986. Unfortunately Halley's Comet moves round the Sun in a retrograde direction – that is to say, opposite to that of the Earth and the other planets. This means that sending a probe to it will be difficult from a guidance and navigation point of view.

All brilliant comets, apart from Halley's, have periods which are so long that to all intents and purposes we may regard them as paying us one visit only. Their orbits are so highly eccentric that they are practically parabolic, and the periods may amount to thousands, tens of thousands, or even millions of years. Obviously, great comets cannot be predicted, and this also applies to the many smaller telescopic comets which have near-parabolic paths.

Great comets were fairly common in the last century; the comet of 1811 had a tail stretching right across the sky, and other brilliant visitors were seen in 1843, 1858, 1861, and 1882 (twice). In 1910 the non-periodical 'Daylight Comet' surpassed Halley's. Since then there has been a relative dearth of brilliant comets, though Bennett's, discovered by the South African amateur astronomer of that name, was conspicuous for some weeks in the spring of 1970. We cannot tell when the next great comet will appear; by the law of averages, one is considerably overdue.

Comets and meteors

Comets are associated with meteor showers, and meteoric debris is spread along cometary orbits. Each time a comet passes at its closest to the Sun, there is evaporation from the icy particles in the head; it is this which produces the tail. Constant wastage means that the short-period comets fade from apparition to apparition, and they must be regarded as short-lived members of the Solar System. Biela's Comet, for instance, was observed to split into two portions in 1846; the twins returned on schedule in 1852, but have not been seen since. The dead comet was replaced, in 1872, by a brilliant shower of meteors. Even today, a century later, a few meteors are seen each November, marking the debris of the comet.

It used to be thought that comets came from outer space, but it is now believed that they are true members of the Solar System, even though their origin is still a matter for debate. Obviously, close-range analysis of their material would be of immense interest, and this is why plans are already being made to send a probe up with the aim of intercepting a comet.

Comet probe

In the painting, we see an unmanned probe reappearing after passing safely through a comet's head or coma. The composition of the gases has been measured, and the nucleus photographed. The high-gain antenna is turned toward the Earth, and is now transmitting information about the hydrogen envelope which surrounds the comet and stretches out for many thousands of miles. Even though this is not a Great Comet, the coma is still considerably larger than the Earth, and even at a modest relative velocity of some eight miles per second the probe has taken over an hour to pass through the comet's coma.

The tail, here fanned out by perspective, is several million miles long. It naturally points away from the Sun, which is just below the bottom right-hand corner of the picture. In the distance are seen the crescents of the Earth and the Moon; of course, these crescents also face the Sun.

Background stars can be seen shining through the comet's tail. This shows that the gases are very tenuous indeed – millions of times less dense than the atmosphere of the Earth. Though comets were dreaded in ancient times, and were thought to be the forerunners of bad news, we now know that they are harmless. Even a direct collision between the Earth and a comet would cause no more than local devastation, since there is little mass except in the small nucleus. Yet our knowledge of comets is still incomplete, and we may hope to learn more when we can make direct contact with one of these strange celestial nomads.

A comet probe *right*
An unmanned probe reappear's after having passed through the coma of the comet. Spectacular though it may sometimes look, a comet has very little mass compared with that of even a small planet, and there is no reason why a probe should not be able to go right through it, though there is always a danger of collision with solid particles. The tail is even less substantial; note how the background stars can be seen through the tail virtually undimmed. The Earth and Moon are visible in the crescent form.

Halley's comet *below*
Halley's Comet is the only bright comet to have a period of less than several centuries. It was visible in 1682, although its appearance had been recorded many times previously, and Edmund Halley calculated its orbit. He found that the path was almost identical with those of comets seen in 1531 and 1607, and came to the conclusion that the comets were one and the same. This series of photographs shows the development and evolution of the tail in 1910.

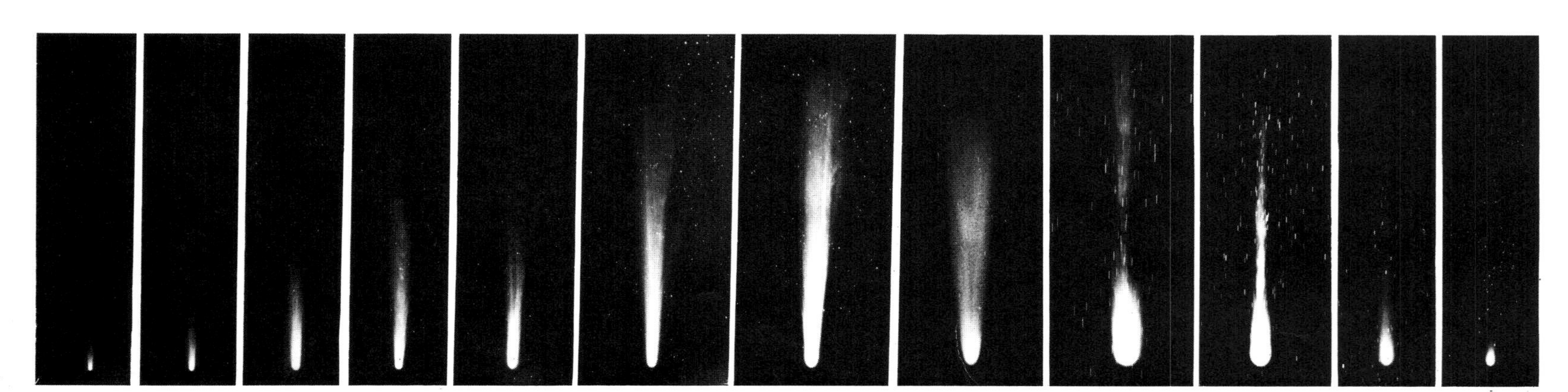

OUR PLACE IN THE GALAXY

Our rockets have taken men to the Moon. Within the next few decades the first explorers will land on Mars, and unmanned probes will voyage out to the cold depths of the Solar System. Yet we must not fall into the trap of supposing that we are 'conquering the universe'. All we are doing is sending our messengers to our own local region. Beyond lie the stars – so far away that to reach them will need new techniques at the moment beyond our understanding.

The Sun is a star. It is no larger, hotter or more luminous than many of the stars visible on any clear night; indeed, astronomers rank it as a dwarf. Although it is of fundamental importance to ourselves, since we belong to its system, it is of no importance whatsoever in the Galaxy considered as a whole. Even the nearest star beyond the Sun is more than 24 million million miles away. Before we can seriously discuss interstellar travel, we must appreciate how vast the Galaxy really is.

Our Sun, a normal star, is over 5,000 million years old. It is attended by a family of planets, of which one – the Earth – is inhabited. There is no reason to doubt that other stars also have planetary systems circling them, and it is only logical to suppose that many of these planets must support life. Unfortunately, planets of other stars cannot be observed directly by means of our present-day equipment. A planet is much smaller than an ordinary star, and has no light of its own; it shines only by reflection. No telescope we have yet built or planned would be capable of showing even a large planet moving round a comparatively close star. We have excellent evidence that such planets exist, but this evidence is, as yet, indirect.

Certainly there are plenty of stars from which to choose. The Galaxy contains approximately 100,000 million suns, of all sizes, luminosities and stages of evolution. Some are immensely powerful, so that they would outshine the Sun just as a searchlight outshines a glow-worm; others are feeble. Some are so huge that they could contain the whole path of the Earth round the Sun, while others are smaller than the Moon. Some are millions of times less dense than the air we breathe, while others are so 'heavy' that many tons of their material could be packed into a space the size of a letter 'o' on this page. And though most of the stars shine steadily for year after year and century after century, some are variable in light, and a few are violently explosive.

Contact across the Galaxy

How are we to get in touch with other civilizations, far away across the Galaxy? We cannot hope for direct contact by means of rocket probes, piloted or automatic. Represent the Earth–Sun distance by one inch, and the nearest star will be four miles away. Moving at velocities we can now attain, a rocket would be thousands of centuries on the journey. The only thing which seems to move quickly enough is light – or, to be more precise, any form of electromagnetic radiation. It is not impossible that we might be able to pick up artificial transmissions from another system, and efforts to do so have already been made, though without success.

The most we could hope to do would be to identify signals sufficiently rhythmical to be classed as non-natural. The distances involved would preclude any exchange of information, even if a suitable code could be worked out. If signals were picked up from, say, a star 10 light-years away, then the signals would already be 10 years old by the time they reached us – and any reply would not arrive at the distant system for a further 10 years. This is an extreme case; there are not many stars as close as this.

The necessary speed

According to modern theory, no material body can move at the velocity of light; but there is no theoretical objection to reaching a speed very close to it. An atomic rocket, able to accelerate over a very long period, may one day be built for interstellar flight. It sounds fantastic as yet – but much less fantastic than reaching Mars would have seemed to Julius Cæsar! Alternatively, some method may be found which does not involve material transfer. It is too early even to speculate about problems of this order, but they may well be tackled during the centuries ahead.

The Galaxy would appear as a flattened system if it could be observed edge-on. The overall diameter is 100,000 light-years, and the shape is rather as shown in the left-hand diagram. The Sun, with its system of planets, lies close to the main plane, but well away from the centre; the distance to the galactic hub is about 32,000 light-years.

Viewed in plan, it would become obvious that the Galaxy is spiral, not unlike a huge Catherine-wheel; the Sun is near the edge of one spiral arm. The Galaxy is rotating, and the Sun takes approximately 225,000,000 years to complete one journey round the centre. This period is sometimes known unofficially as the cosmic year. One cosmic year ago, the most advanced creatures on Earth were amphibians; even the fearsome dinosaurs were yet to make their entry on the terrestrial scene.

The Galaxy contains many features besides individual stars. There are, for instance, clouds of dust and gas which are known as nebulæ; the most famous example is in the constellation of Orion. It is thought that a star begins its career by condensing out of the thinly-spread interstellar material, and that nebulæ may be regarded as stellar birthplaces.

In the spiral arms of the Galaxy there is considerable interstellar matter, and many nebulæ. The most brilliant stars are extremely hot, and white or bluish-white. Regions of this sort are known as Population I, a term due originally to the late Walter Baade. Elsewhere – for instance, in some regions near the galactic centre – there is much less material available to form fresh stars, and the most conspicuous objects are large, powerful red stars. These regions are classed as Population II.

How a star develops

With this information, we can begin to examine the way in which a star develops. As we have seen, it begins by condensing out of nebular material. At first it does not shine; but as it contracts, under the influence of gravity, its inner regions become hot. When the temperature has risen sufficiently, nuclear reactions begin. The star settles down to a long period of stable radiation; it is said to belong to the Main Sequence. This is the present condition of the Sun.

The production of energy

Stars are not 'burning' in the usual sense of the term. Inside the Sun, nuclei of hydrogen atoms are combining to form nuclei of the second lightest element, helium. Each time a helium nucleus is formed from hydrogen, a little energy is released and a little mass is lost. It is this energy which keeps the Sun shining; the mass-loss amounts to 4 million tons per second, but although this seems very rapid we may be confident that the Sun will continue radiating steadily for at least 6,000 million years in the future. Eventually, of course, its supply of available hydrogen will begin to fail, and the Sun will change radically. It will become a red giant, and for a period will be much more luminous than it is today, though its surface will be cooler.

We cannot expect life on Earth to survive the Sun's change into a red giant; but if humanity still exists, no doubt some way will be found to avoid destruction.

Our Galaxy is by no means the only one. At distances of millions of light-years we can see others, many of which are spiral in form. The famous Andromeda Spiral, which is dimly visible to the naked eye, is a spiral much larger than ours, and so far away that its light takes 2,200,000 years to reach us. Yet even this system belongs to what we call the Local Group – a collection of over twenty galaxies making up a stable unit.

No telescope can show a star as anything but a point of light, and our information comes chiefly from instruments based on the principle of the spectroscope. Starlight is split up, and we can find out what elements are present in the stars themselves. We can also discover whether the stars are approaching us or are moving away. The spectrum of a galaxy is made of the combined spectra of its millions of stars, but it can be interpreted; and it has been found that all the galaxies, apart from those in the Local Group, are racing away from us. For instance, a galaxy known by its catalogue number of 3C-295 is receding at almost half the velocity of light. It is believed by many astronomers that some enigmatical objects known as quasars, which are smaller than galaxies but may be essentially similar to them, are even more remote and receding even more rapidly.

This does not imply that we are in any special position. The entire universe is expanding. Whether this will continue indefinitely we cannot tell, neither do we know anything about the way in which the universe was created. All we can do is to study its evolution; we are totally ignorant of the fundamental 'beginning',

From Earth we obviously cannot see our Galaxy in its entirety. The centre of the system lies in the direction of the wonderful star-clouds in the constella-

The Milky Way Galaxy
Below left The Milky Way Galaxy, as it would be seen edge-on. It is a flattened system, 100,000 light-years in diameter; the Sun lies 32,000 light-years from the hub. Surrounding the main system is the 'galactic halo', made up of compact globular clusters as well as isolated stars.
Below The Galaxy as it would be seen in plan. In this view the spiral arms are shown; the Sun is situated near the edge of one of them. As yet we cannot pretend that we know why spiral arms form, or whether they are permanent features throughout most of the evolutionary cycle of a galaxy.

tion of Sagittarius (the Archer), but our view of the centre itself is cut off; there is too much interstellar material between it and ourselves, so that light-waves are absorbed. Longer-wavelength radiations, known as radio waves, can however come through, and are collected and analyzed by radio telescopes such as the famous paraboloid at Jodrell Bank. On the other hand, we can have overall views of many other spirals, and so we can form a very good idea of what our Galaxy would look like if it could be seen from beyond.

In the painting, it is night on an inhabited planet of a 'stray' star moving some 200,000 light-years outside the Galaxy. The spiral nature of the arms, glowing with hot blue Population I stars, is clearly shown, as is the central hub, dominated by the cooler but very luminous red giants characteristic of Population II. Individual stars cannot be seen at this distance; only the star-clouds are visible, and between the arms are dark patches – dust-clouds which are not lit up by stars, and which may be called dark nebulæ. Well above the horizon, to the left in the painting, is the solitary moon of our hypothetical planet, casting its radiance on to the landscape below.

Life on such a planet

What beings could live here? This is a question we cannot yet answer. If a planet has a suitably even temperature, if there is atmosphere and water, it is reasonable to suppose that life will develop; and if conditions are similar to those on Earth, intelligent beings could well be similar to ourselves. If the environment is different, then the life-forms will be different, though they may be equally advanced – or even more so.

On this planet of a stray star, one feature will be missing from the night sky: the Milky Way. To us on Earth, the Milky Way is a glorious band of light stretching from one horizon to the other. It is made up of stars, together with cosmic clouds both bright and dark – but the stars in it are not crowded together, as they appear. The Milky Way is mainly an effect of perspective. When we look along the main plane of the Galaxy we see many stars in much the same direction, and it is this which produces the band of radiance. On a world outside the Galaxy nothing comparable would be seen; part of the sky would be almost starless, but in compensation there would be the glorious spiral shown here.

Through a telescope, individual stars could be seen. One of them, an insignificant yellow dwarf, is here just above the planet's moon – and indeed lost in its glare. Outwardly it has nothing to single it out for special attention. How could alien beings tell that this obscure star is the centre of a planetary system, and that the inhabitants of one of those planets have already taken their first steps into space? In fact, their view of the Sun would be 200,000 years out of date, and must go back to a time before civilization on Earth had begun.

We can hardly doubt that many alien astronomers are at this moment looking at the Sun from their observatories built upon planets of other stars. And one day, contact may be made.

Night scene *above*
An inhabited planet of a star outside the Galaxy, moving at 200,000 light-years from the main system. A moon of the planet appears to the left, well above the horizon. The brilliance and beauty of the spiral would more than compensate for the fact that the rest of the sky would be very sparsely scattered with stars.

DISTANT STARS

The nearest of all the bright stars is Alpha Centauri, which is never visible from Europe, but is a brilliant object in southern skies; of all the stars only Sirius and Canopus outshine it. It is made up of two components, moving round their common centre of gravity and making up what is termed a binary system. The distance of the Alpha Centauri pair is 4.3 light-years. (One light-year is equal to 5,880,000 million miles.)

There is a third member of the Alpha Centauri system. This is Proxima, which is much fainter than its luminous companions; although it is the nearest star to the Earth, approximately one-tenth of a light-year closer than Alpha Centauri, it is far too dim to be seen without a telescope. It is a celestial glow-worm – a feeble red dwarf.

Proxima Centauri is a star of very different type from the Sun. Its surface temperature is much lower, and its total luminosity is only 0.0001 of that of the Sun. Its evolutionary career, too, must have been different, simply because of its lesser mass. If our Sun were as feeble as Proxima, a planet moving at a distance of 93,000,000 miles would be a chilly world indeed – much too cold to support life of our kind. Therefore, if Proxima has a habitable planet, we must look for it in a region much closer to the red surface.

Perhaps it is misleading to say 'look for it', because even if Proxima were attended by a planet as large as Jupiter we would have no hope of seeing it with our present-day telescopes. Fortunately, there are other methods. Relatively close stars have perceptible individual or proper motions, and shift slowly against the background of more distant stars; Proxima does so at the rate of 3.75 seconds of arc per year. This means that it takes 600 years to move by an amount equal to the apparent diameter of the Moon as seen from Earth. Slow though this motion may seem, it is easily measurable from year to year.

Barnard's Star

Another faint red dwarf, Barnard's Star, has an even greater proper motion (over 10 seconds of arc per year) even though it is more remote than Proxima. Barnard's Star is not, however, moving smoothly. It is 'weaving' its way along, and it has been found that this irregular motion is caused by the presence of an invisible body which moves round the star and pulls it out of position. The mass of the companion is too small for it to be a star, and so it is presumably a planet; indeed, there may even be two planets accompanying Barnard's Star. This is a reliable indication that the retinue of planets moving round our Sun is very far from being unique.

There have been suspicions that Proxima, too, may have a planet moving round it. The evidence at present is slender, but the planet may exist. The painting shows the view which might be expected from it. The planet is relatively near its weak red sun, around which (it is calculated) it orbits in 10–12 days; the limb of Proxima is not sharp, but is clearly diffuse. The landscape is completely hypothetical; we see eroded black, basaltic rocks, as lonely and desolate as anything on our Moon, though the planet retains a thin atmosphere which is replenished by occasional feeble bursts of gas from volcanic vents. No sedimentary rocks hint at past life, though water survives in a lake fringed by glittering ice-crystals. In the sky a solitary moon is silhouetted in transit against the dull redness of Proxima. The two bright stars of Alpha Centauri are 'behind' us, and at the moment add no perceptible illumination, though they will be brilliant during the planet's period of night. Perhaps this scene is duplicated many times on planets of other red dwarf stars in the Galaxy.

Planet of Proxima Centauri *above*
The scene from a hypothetical planet orbiting Proxima Centauri. The landscape is desolate; in the dark sky the stars shine down, with the constellation patterns very similar to those we know. To the right of the black disk betraying the transit of a moon we see the W of Cassiopeia, but there is an extra star; this is the Sun, which from Proxima will be conspicuous but not glaringly so. It will convert the W into a constellation which inhabitants or future interstellar travellers may well nickname 'the Switchback'. The Southern Cross, below the horizon in this painting, will lack one of its two 'pointers' – Alpha Centauri itself, which will appear as a pair of distant suns casting light on to the bleak rocks.

DISTANT STARS 2

Though there must surely be millions of 'other Earths' in the Galaxy, not all stars are suited to be the centres of planetary systems. The most likely candidates are stable, single stars such as the Sun. A planet moving round a binary star would have a strange, uncomfortable climate – unless the two suns were close together and luminous enough to warm a planet circling at a comparatively great distance.

Binary systems of all kinds are known. Sometimes the component members of the pair are very widely separated, so that the mutual revolution period amounts to thousands or even millions of years. In other cases the two suns are almost in contact, so that each is drawn out into the shape of an egg. From Earth we cannot see the individual members of such a pair, but spectroscopic observations can give us a surprising amount of information. Beta Lyræ, in the constellation of the Harp, is one such binary, but many others of the same type are known.

In 1667 an Italian astronomer named Montanari noticed that there was something very strange about Algol, a fairly bright star in the constellation of Perseus. Stars are graded according to their magnitudes, relating to their apparent brightness (not their real luminosity); very bright stars are of magnitude 1, while the faintest stars normally visible to the naked eye are of magnitude 6. Algol is normally of the second magnitude, roughly equal to the Pole Star. Montanari found that every two and a half days it gave a very slow 'wink', taking some hours to fade down to below the third magnitude and staying at minimum for twenty minutes before regaining its lost lustre. By what seems to have been sheer coincidence, the Arab astronomers of a thousand years ago knew the star we call Algol as 'the Demon Star'.

Montanari did not know the cause of this strange behaviour, but Algol's fluctuations were explained in 1783 by John Goodricke, a young deaf-mute astronomer. Algol is not genuinely variable in light. It is a binary; one component is larger but less brilliant than the other. Every two and a half days the fainter component partially eclipses or hides the brighter, as shown in the series of diagrams above, so that the total light we receive from the system drops. There is a much less obvious drop in the light when the brighter component passes between the fainter star and ourselves.

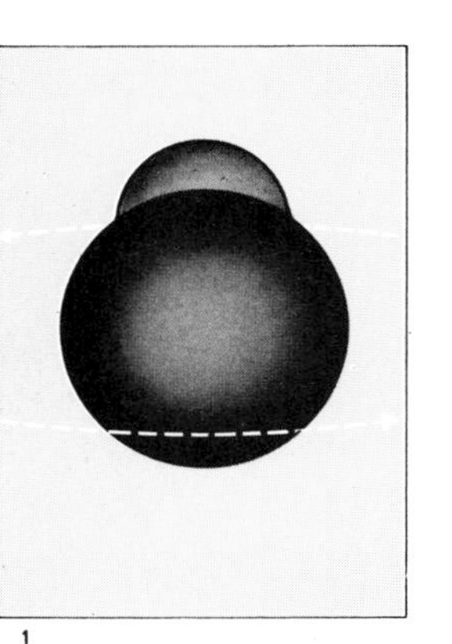

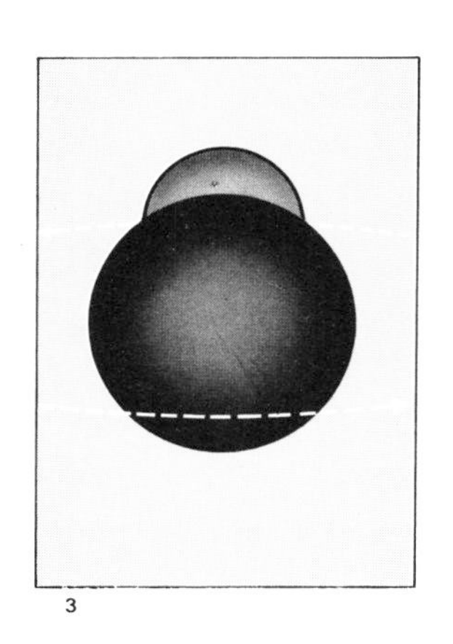

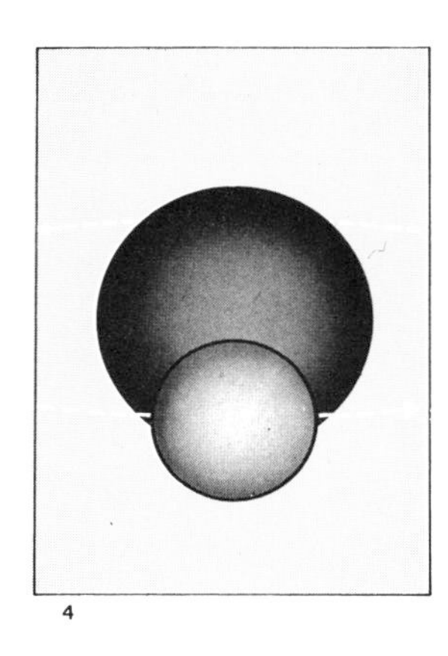

Diagram of an eclipsing binary *above*
The eclipsing binary Algol. In the first and third positions the smaller but more luminous star is partly hidden by the larger, cooler component, and from Earth we see the principal eclipse; from the second magnitude Algol declines to below the third. In the second and fourth positions the faint component is partly hidden by the more brilliant. The result is a slight decrease in the light we receive; this secondary minimum is detectable by means of sensitive instruments known as photometers.

Today many of these eclipsing binaries are known. They are extremely valuable to astronomers, because they can provide information about the sizes and masses of the individual stars in the binary. With a binary system in which there is no eclipse, we can find out only the combined masses of the two components. Of course, there is no real difference between an eclipsing and a non-eclipsing binary; it is merely a question of the angle at which the orbit is tilted relative to the Earth.

Beta Lyræ

The second eclipsing binary to be discovered was Beta Lyræ, sometimes still known by its old proper name of Sheliak. It is easy to find, since it lies close to the brilliant blue star Vega, which is almost overhead as seen from Britain and the northern United States during summer evenings. In fact Beta Lyræ is much the more distant of the two. Vega is a mere 27 light-years from us, while the distance of Beta Lyræ is about 1,100 light-years; we see it as it was in the reign of Alfred the Great.

Like Algol, Beta Lyræ has two main components, much too close together to be seen individually. The two are less unequal than in the case of Algol, and so the behaviour is different. When we construct a light-curve, plotting time against the changing magnitude, we find the effect shown in the diagram. Variations are always going on; there are alternative deep and shallow minima. During a deep minimum the more luminous component is partly hidden by the fainter; at a shallow minimum it is the fainter star which is covered up. The revolution period is 12 days 22 hours 22 minutes, and this appears to be increasing at ten seconds per year.

The larger component of Beta Lyræ is hot and bluish-white. The secondary is less hot, but its spectrum has not been observed, so that we are by no means certain what it is like. It has always been taken to be a star with a surface rather hotter than that of the Sun. Recently there have been suggestions that it may be an altogether different type of object – a 'black hole', or collapsed star; but for the moment we may regard Beta Lyræ as a normal eclipsing binary.

The scene from a hypothetical planet orbiting the pair is shown in the painting. It is an incredible spectacle. The two suns are so close together that they almost touch, and an observer on the planet would see their distorted shapes. Moreover, the stars are surrounded by streamers of gas. Glowing hydrogen is ejected from the equator of the larger star, which is spinning round rapidly. Some of the material is 'caught' by the fainter, smaller star; there is a constant loss of material into space, so that the overall effect is that of an expanding spiral. We are observing from a deep crevasse on our planet; the shadows and the colour effects are ever-changing.

The planet's climate

What kind of climate could be expected on a planet moving round a system like this, and what sort of life could conceivably evolve there? We must assume that the planet has an atmosphere if there is to be any life, but the hotter star of Beta Lyræ radiates strongly in the short-wave end of the spectrum, and some of these radiations would be lethal to terrestrial-type life were they not effectively screened. The planet would have to be far enough from the central pair to avoid the effects of the gas-streaming, even though the ejected material is certainly very rarefied. The orbit of the planet would be fairly stable, since from a gravitational point of view the two suns, almost or quite in contact, would act as one mass, but there would be wide variations in surface temperature if the plane of the orbit were such that the suns mutually eclipsed each other at each revolution. It would certainly be unwise to claim that no life could exist on a planet of Beta Lyræ, but it is logical to say that the chances are lower than with a single star of solar type. On the other hand, there is no reason why planets in the system could not be visited – once the problems of interstellar travel have been solved!

Planet of Beta Lyræ *right*
The scene from a hypothetical planet orbiting Beta Lyræ; we are looking out from a crevasse on the surface. The sky is dominated by the twin stars and the spiral of expanding gas.

The view from the planet

Beta Lyræ may be an exceptional object, but there are many other binaries where the view from an orbiting planet would be very much as shown in the painting. Beyond the twins, with their streamers of gas, would lie the other stars of the Galaxy, but this time the star-patterns would be unfamiliar to anyone used to the sky of Earth. The situation is not the same as from Proxima, which is relatively so close to us that the overall view would be much the same as ours. Beta Lyræ, remember, is over 1,000 light-years away, so that everything would be changed. The Sun would be a very dim object much too faint to be seen with the naked eye by an observer with sight equal to ours.

Because Beta Lyræ is a much less stable system than that of Alpha Centauri (and, of course, far less stable than the Sun), its evolution must have been quicker, and neither does it have so long an expectation of 'life' before drastic changes occur within it. If there is a life-bearing planet, alterations in the twin suns will certainly destroy this life long before Earth becomes uninhabitable.

With a Beta Lyræ-type binary in which the components are more widely separated, the chances of finding a planet become less, because the two stars would not act as a single controlling mass, and the orbit of the planet would be erratic, resulting in wild fluctuations of temperature. Sometimes one sun would be close, sometimes the other; then there would be periods when both stars shone together, scorching the surface of the planet in a blaze of heat. Yet there must be worlds like this across the Galaxy; and in the distant future it may be that some of them will be explored by men who have travelled hundreds or thousands of light-years across the depths of interstellar space.

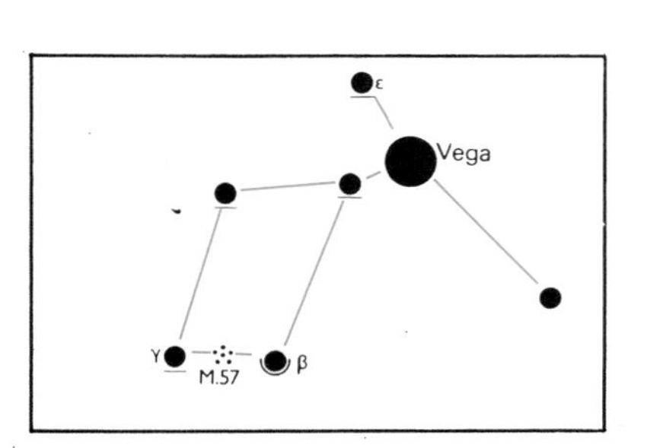

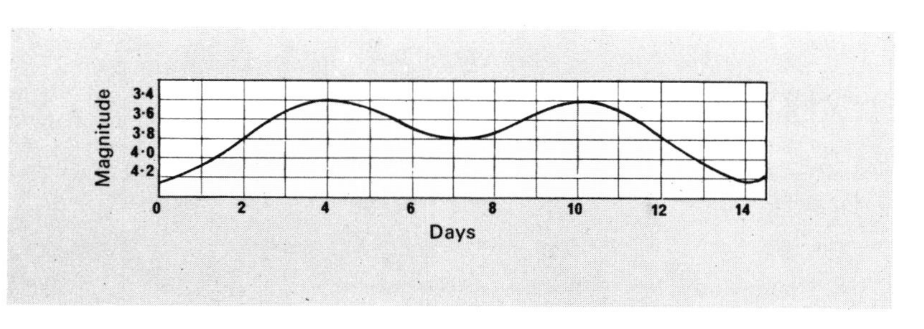

Beta Lyræ
Left Light-curve of Beta Lyræ. The period is just over twelve days, and includes two maxima; the minima are alternately deep and shallow, as the two members of the binary are much less unequal than with Algol. M.57 is the Ring Nebula, seen in a photograph on p. 56.

Far left Position of Beta Lyræ. It lies near the brilliant Vega, and forms a pair with the third-magnitude star Gamma Lyræ. At its brightest, Beta is slightly inferior to Gamma.

DISTANT STARS 3

Of all the stars the huge red giants are among the most remarkable. It used to be thought that they were comparatively young, but we now know that they are old; they have used up their hydrogen 'fuel', and are shining because heavy elements are being synthesized inside them. An extreme example – such as Zeta Aurigæ, shown in the painting – may have a diameter hundreds of times greater than that of the Sun; indeed, Zeta Aurigæ could contain the whole of the Solar System out as far as the asteroid belt. If red giants evolve from Main Sequence stars (and of this there is virtually no doubt) they will swallow up their inner planets; surviving planets must be orbiting at a respectful distance from their swollen sun. From being cold worlds, they must have become searing hot, and the prospects for the survival of any life-forms on them do not seem to be high. With Zeta Aurigæ the situation is complicated by a binary companion: a very hot bluish star much more powerful than the Sun.

There are no giant or supergiant stars anywhere near the Sun. All our close stellar neighbours are dwarfs – even Sirius in the Great Dog, which looks so magnificent in our skies, is a humble Main Sequence star. Therefore, even if and when interstellar flight becomes possible, it will not be for a long time that we can investigate the planetary systems of giants – assuming that such systems exist.

Planets of giant stars are likely to be uncomfortable places so far as climate is concerned. Even if the central sun is a single star rather than a binary such as Zeta Aurigæ, it is quite likely to be variable. Many of the red giants and Main Sequence. This is the present condition of the Sun, where the temperature near the core is of the order of 13 to 14 million degrees Centigrade. Hydrogen is being steadily converted into helium, and the output is steady – discounting very minor variations over a long period, causing the changes in temperature of the Ice Ages which have affected our world at intervals throughout geological history.

The state of balance

After thousands of millions of years there is no more available hydrogen in the core. Up to this time the star has been in a state of balance between gravity, has left the Main Sequence, and has moved off into the giant branch – to the upper right in the diagram below. The yellow, white or bluish sun has become a red giant.

The Hertzsprung-Russell diagram

The diagram given here is of great importance to theoretical astrophysicists. It is known as a Hertzsprung-Russell or H-R Diagram, in honour of the two astronomers who drew it up more than half a century ago. Originally it was thought that a star 'slipped down' the Main Sequence from the top left to bottom right of the diagram, shrinking steadily and becoming weaker; but we Even if the Earth survives, it will become much too hot to retain any atmosphere or surface water, so that life here cannot continue indefinitely.

Zeta Aurigæ, shown in the painting, has already reached the red giant stage; any inner planets will have been destroyed. Only the more remote planets in such a system can still exist, and even these are likely to be uninhabitable. When the first explorers reach them, the scene will be one of total sterility, but also one of weird beauty; with Zeta Aurigæ, the combination of the red supergiant and the hot bluish companion would produce colour effects which defy description.

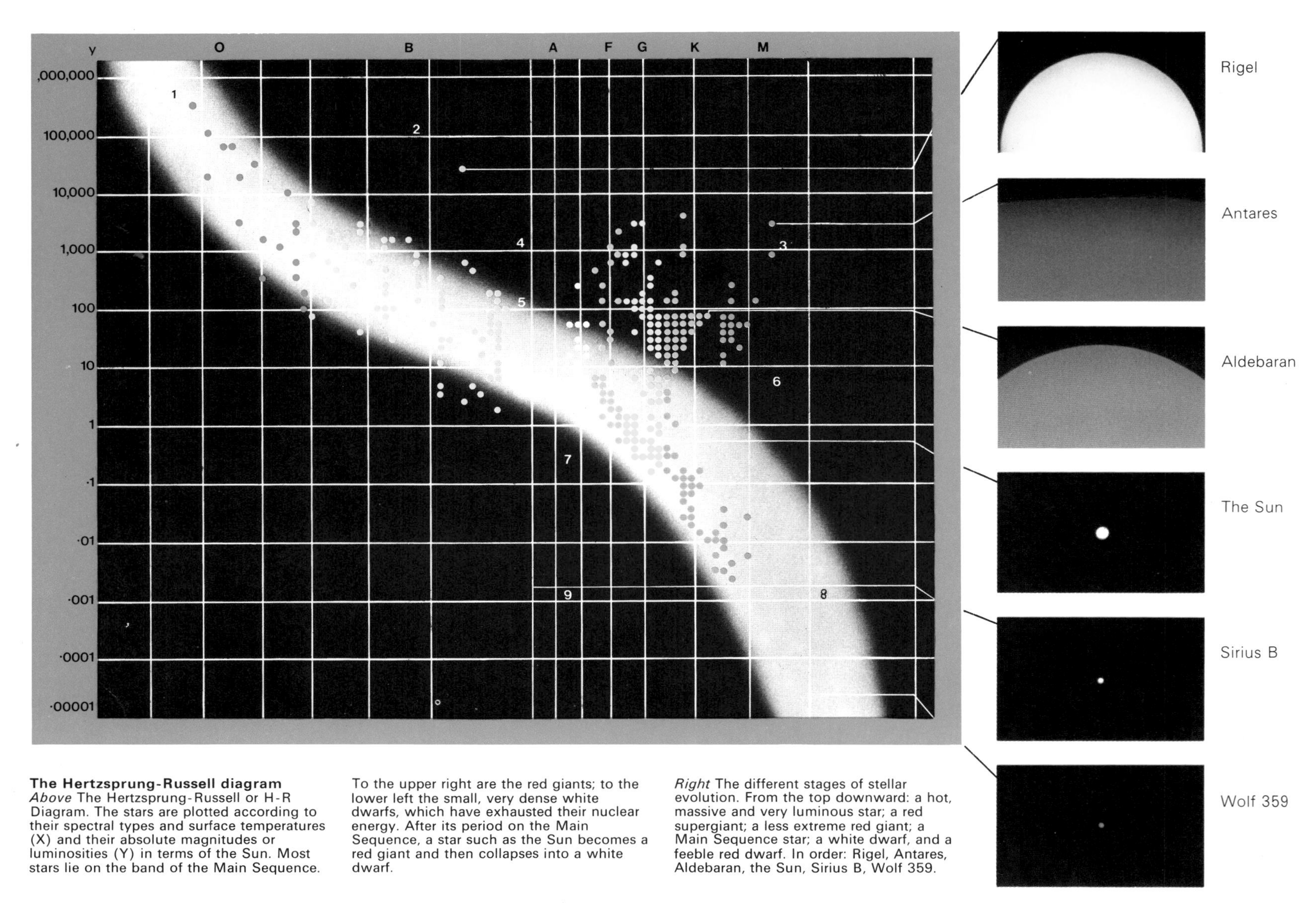

The Hertzsprung-Russell diagram
Above The Hertzsprung-Russell or H-R Diagram. The stars are plotted according to their spectral types and surface temperatures (X) and their absolute magnitudes or luminosities (Y) in terms of the Sun. Most stars lie on the band of the Main Sequence. To the upper right are the red giants; to the lower left the small, very dense white dwarfs, which have exhausted their nuclear energy. After its period on the Main Sequence, a star such as the Sun becomes a red giant and then collapses into a white dwarf.

Right The different stages of stellar evolution. From the top downward: a hot, massive and very luminous star; a red supergiant; a less extreme red giant; a Main Sequence star; a white dwarf, and a feeble red dwarf. In order: Rigel, Antares, Aldebaran, the Sun, Sirius B, Wolf 359.

supergiants fluctuate considerably in their radiation output over relatively short periods of a few weeks or months. This variation is intrinsic, and is not due to an eclipsing companion as with Algol or Beta Lyræ – even though it is possible that some red giants may also have companions.

As we have seen, a star begins its luminous career by condensing out of interstellar material. When its inner temperature is sufficiently high, nuclear reactions begin, and the star joins the tending to pull all the material to the centre, and radiation and gas pressure, tending to distend the globe. When the production of energy from the hydrogen-into-helium process is halted, the star begins to collapse, but the process does not get very far. As the core temperature rises still further, the helium which has been accumulated there begins to undergo reactions in its turn. These are succeeded by yet others; meanwhile the outer layers of the star have expanded, cooling and changing colour. The star now know that this is wrong. Red giants are older than Main Sequence stars, or are at least more advanced in their cycle of evolution.

The Sun

A star such as the Sun will go through its red giant stage after leaving the Main Sequence. The Sun may become at least 100 times as luminous as it is now, though its surface temperature will be lower; it will swell out, engulfing Mercury, Venus and probably the Earth.

Planet of Zeta Aurigæ *right*
Intriguing bi-coloured shadows on an imaginary planet of the eclipsing binary Zeta Aurigæ. This fantastic system consists of a vast red supergiant over 200,000,000 miles in diameter, together with a hot bluish-white star with a diameter of 3,000,000 miles; this hot star is much more powerful than the Sun. In the painting, the blue star is about to be eclipsed; its light is already dimmed as it passes through the tenuous envelope of gas surrounding the supergiant. The surface of the red star is obscured by an interlacing network of glowing prominences. The hypothetical planet in the painting is 700,000,000 miles from the red supergiant.

DISTANT STARS 4

Binary pairs are of various types; sometimes the two components are almost touching, as with Beta Lyræ, while in other cases the members of the pair are a very long way away from each other. As well as physical doubles, the Galaxy also contains triple and multiple stars; Zeta Cancri, shown in the painting, is a splendid example of a triple system with components of contrasting colours. The two close stars are wider apart than in the case of Beta Lyræ, but tidal distortion still pulls out each member into an egg-shaped form.

Seen from the Earth, Zeta Cancri appears as a rather obscure star in the ill-defined constellation of the Crab. It is of the fifth magnitude, so that it is distinctly visible with the naked eye on a clear night. Through a reasonably powerful telescope it is seen to consist of two stars, one orange and one white, which make up a binary pair with a revolution period of 59.6 years. Further away, and easily detectable in a small telescope, is a yellow star, orbiting the primary pair in a period of 1,150 years. The paths of the three members of the system are decidedly complicated, as shown in the diagram, so that a planet will have a variable and erratic orbit, with wide ranges in temperature and illumination.

The scene shown in the painting is a faithful representation of what would be observed from a planet of the Zeta Cancri system. Here, even more than with Beta Lyræ, we have spectacular lighting effects, because the three components are quite similar in luminosity. since been driven off, so that the sky is star-studded and black even though the two suns loom so large. The distant member appears as a small sun, and is surrounded by a swarm of cosmic dust, recalling our own Sun's Zodiacal Light. Because of the long revolution period, the distant companion would seem to move very slowly against the starry background. When the planet moves between it and the close pair, there can be no true darkness; 'night' will occur for only part of the planet's 'year'.

Evolution of the system

The orange component of Zeta Cancri has already left the Main Sequence, and moved off to the upper right part of the H-R Diagram into the giant branch. Here, too, we must therefore expect that the planetary system will have suffered severely, with the inner members being destroyed and the formerly chill outer planets becoming suddenly super-tropical. Interstellar travellers will indeed

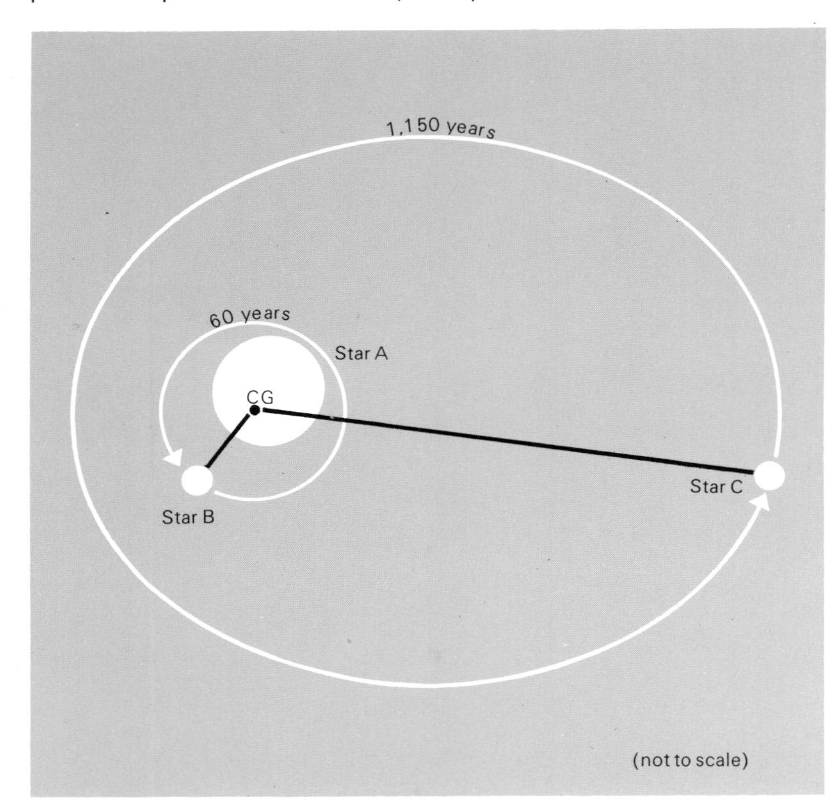

The smaller member of the close pair is white, but in the painting it appears bluish, because of the contrast effects in the system. There may well be a 'bridge' of tenuous material between the white star and the orange giant, which is much larger than the Sun even though not nearly so extreme an example of a giant star as the red component of Zeta Aurigæ.

Lifeless planet

A planet in a system of this kind is likely to be lifeless; here we see a volcanic-type landscape, with a trace of activity remaining in the vent to the left of the painting. Lava-flows cover the barren surface, and any atmosphere has long find very strange and beautiful sights awaiting them.

Triple systems are spectacular by any standards, but in the Galaxy we find groups containing four, five or more components. Castor, the fainter member of the two famous Twins, is multiple; there are two main components, each of which is itself a close binary, and at a much greater distance there is a third component which is again a close binary. Castor therefore consists of six stars, four brilliant and two dim red dwarfs – though the colours are not so sharply contrasting as with Zeta Cancri or Zeta Aurigæ.

From multiple stars we come on to loose or open clusters, of which there are plenty in the Galaxy. Much the most famous is that of the Pleiades or Seven Sisters, which is very prominently visible with the naked eye; it lies in the constellation of Taurus (the Bull), not far from the red giant Aldebaran.

The Pleiades cluster contains at least seven stars visible without optical aid (keen-sighted people can see more than a dozen), and the total number of stars exceeds 200. The distance of the cluster is 410 light-years; the leading stars, headed by the third-magnitude Alcyone, are hot and bluish-white. Mixed in with the cluster-stars is a gaseous nebula, which shines by reflection and is well shown only in photographs taken with large telescopes.

Many other open clusters are known, some of which are visible with the naked eye; for instance we have the Hyades round Aldebaran (though Aldebaran is not itself a member of the cluster), Præsepe in Cancer, and the lovely 'Jewel Box' round Kappa Crucis in the Southern Cross. Yet even inside these clusters, the individual stars are still widely separated – by many thousands of millions of miles – and collisions can hardly ever occur. It has been calculated that an ordinary star has very little risk of suffering a collision, or even a close encounter, with another star during the whole of its lifetime.

Yet if it were possible to go to a planet inside an open cluster, the night sky would be glorious, with many stars brighter than Sirius appears to us. Some of them would cast perceptible shadows, and darkness would be unknown.

The fear of darkness

How would this affect any life-forms on such a planet? Of course we can only speculate; but we can imagine that darkness would be their greatest fear, simply because it would not occur except in places closed off from the sky. In the daytime there would be the glare of the local sun – perhaps a bluish-white star, though clusters also contain red giants and feeble dwarfs. After the sun had set, there would be the hundreds of thousands of night-time suns, still casting a brilliant light across the surface of the planet.

No cluster lies near us in the Galaxy, so that before we can send astronauts to such a place we must learn how to travel hundreds of light-years. As yet we have no idea of how it might be done; but the prospect is not so fantastic as it may sound. Once the method has been found, it may be a relatively minor step between travelling four light-years and travelling four hundred. Soon after we have sent our pioneers out to Proxima and Alpha Centauri, we may also be able to send them to the vividly-coloured system of Zeta Cancri or to the inner part of the cluster of the Pleiades. Our Sun will have faded into the distance; but there will be suns in plenty to take its place.

The system of Zeta Cancri
Left Diagram of the orbits of the triple star system depicted in the painting opposite. The system rotates about the centre of gravity which is offset from the centre of the main planet. Consequently the orbit of any planets in the system would be subject to a differing gravitational attraction.

Right View from a planet orbiting the triple system of Zeta Cancri. There are three suns; a close pair made up of an orange giant together with a white companion (here looking bluish, by contrast), and a distant yellow star. Gravity distorts the close pair into elliptical shapes, and there is probably an exchange of material from their outer layers. The distances are not represented to an exact scale.

DISTANT STARS 5

Sometimes a bright star will appear unexpectedly in the sky, remaining conspicuous for a few days, weeks or even months before fading away to its former obscurity. This is known as a nova. The name is rather misleading; 'nova' means 'new', and a nova is not a new star. It is merely a dim star which has undergone a sudden outburst, flaring up temporarily to many times its usual brilliance.

Novæ have been regarded as stars which are collapsing from the red giant stage into white dwarfs, but it seems that they are not numerous enough to represent a typical stage in stellar evolution, even though they are reasonably common. Thus bright novæ were seen in 1901 (Perseus), 1918 (Aquila), 1934 (Hercules), 1942 (Puppis) and so on. Many old novæ are known to be close binaries. Obviously a nova outburst would have a disastrous effect upon any orbiting planets, and the painting shows the scene upon a world which has narrowly escaped destruction.

Because we live on a planet moving round a star which is in a stable condition, we tend to think of the universe as being quiet. Yet this is wrong; the universe is restless, and tremendous outbursts do occur. After it leaves the Main Sequence, between 6,000 and 8,000 million years from now, our Sun too will become erratic – and if mankind survives, it must plan its escape before its formerly friendly star becomes a red giant.

The change will not be sudden, and there will be plenty of warning. With a nova outburst the reverse is true. The luminosity increases in a matter of hours or days, and is unpredictable. So far as we can tell, the Sun is not the kind of star liable to suffer a nova outburst – certainly not while it remains on the Main Sequence; but we cannot be sure that the same will always be true. If an outburst happened, there could be no hope for Earth or Mars, and remote Pluto would change from its frozen isolation into a scorched wilderness.

The cause of a nova

We cannot pretend to be certain about the precise cause of a nova outbreak, but apparently an excessive quantity of energy is suddenly produced below the star's surface. A superficial layer is violently ejected, though this does not affect the main body of the star. As the layer is shot outward, it expands into a shell; its surface area increases, and so, therefore, does the apparent luminosity of the star. Other shells may follow, and as the nova fades it may be seen to be surrounded by an expanding gas-cloud. This was the case with the brightest nova of modern times, which blazed out in Aquila in 1918 and at maximum rivalled Sirius. Before becoming too faint to be observable, the shell had expanded to a diameter of 10,000 times the Earth's distance from the Sun.

In the painting, the nova outburst is too distant to have vaporized the imagined planet, as it would the inner planets of the system; but the effects of the tremendous blast are evident enough. If the planet used to support life, it can do so no longer. A nova explosion leaves a system ruined and dead for all time.

Worlds like this must surely exist in the Galaxy, and will one day be visited by interstellar travellers. Automatic transmitting stations will be set up there, and the post-nova behaviour of the star will be studied. A few stars, such as T Coronæ in the constellation of the Northern Crown, have been seen to suffer more than one nova outburst (with T Coronæ, in 1866 and again in 1946), but generally speaking it is likely that a star becomes a nova only once in its career.

A star of solar mass will eventually collapse into a very small, dense object known as a white dwarf. Nuclear energy is exhausted; the atomic particles are packed together, and the result is that a cupful of white dwarf material would weigh many tons. No doubt white dwarfs are among the commonest of all stars in the Galaxy, though their faintness means that we can observe only the nearer ones. The most famous white dwarf is the companion of Sirius, which is 10,000 times less luminous than the brilliant primary – and yet has a mass approximately equal to that of the Sun, packed into a globe only 24,000 miles in diameter.

A white dwarf

A white dwarf has been described as a bankrupt star. It can do nothing except cool and fade; after a long interval of perhaps 500 thousand million years it will have no luminosity left, and will become a black dwarf – the ghost of a star, wandering unseen across the vastness of the Galaxy, perhaps still attended by the remnants of its planetary system. These worlds will indeed be desolate.

This is the final fate of a solar type star, but the death of a much more massive star is spectacular. The nuclear reactions may 'run wild', resulting in a supernova outburst in which the star blows most of its material away into space. At its brightest, a supernova may be radiating up to 15,000 million times as much energy as the Sun, and no planet, however remote from the original star, could hope to survive such a blaze.

Four supernovæ have been seen in our Galaxy during the past thousand years. The last was Kepler's Star of 1604, so that none has appeared since the invention of the telescope. However, supernovæ are so luminous that they may be observed in other galaxies millions of light-years away. One, S Andromedæ of 1885, burst out in the Great Spiral, and reached the fringe of naked-eye visibility.

The Crab Nebula

The supernova in the constellation of Taurus observed by Chinese astronomers in the year 1054 has left an expanding gas-cloud known as the Crab Nebula. It is visible in a small telescope; photographs taken with giant instruments reveal an intricate structure, and it has been found that the gas is still spreading rapidly outward from the old explosion-centre. As well as sending us visible light, the Crab is a very powerful source of radio waves, and more recently it has also been found to emit X-radiation. It is a celestial laboratory, and to astrophysicists probably the most informative object in the entire sky. Its distance from us is 6,000 light-years.

Inside the Crab Nebula is an extraordinary object known as a pulsar. This is extremely small – only a few miles in diameter – and is sending out rapidly-varying radio waves. Like other pulsars, it is thought to be a neutron star, which is even more extreme than a white dwarf. If the contraction of a massive star proceeds far enough, the protons and electrons will combine into neutrons – and the resulting density is incredibly high; a thousand million tons could be packed into a globe the size of a marble.

The pulsar in the Crab Nebula is the only one to have been identified with a visible object – a faint, flashing speck of light – but it is likely that other pulsars, detected because of their radio emission, are also the remains of old supernovæ. The long-wavelength radiations seem to vibrate, often in periods of less than a second, so that the effect is one of 'ticking'; when pulsars were first identified, in 1967, there was a brief period when astronomers seriously considered whether the signals might be artificial transmissions. Nowadays this idea has been completely discounted, and it is believed that a pulsar is a rotating neutron star – the period of rotation corresponding to the frequency of the 'ticks'.

Even in the far-away future, it seems impossible that an interstellar traveller could ever invade the Crab Nebula, with its medley of radiations, or approach a neutron star. If close-range studies of these fantastic objects are to be carried out, it must be by some method which does not involve travel in a material sense. This is something totally beyond our comprehension as yet. In this book we have based our descriptions and the paintings upon the facts as we know them, and although some of the details may be wrong we are confident that the scenes given here are not far from the truth – as close, perhaps, as the 'lunar landscapes' painted by artists (including the present illustrator) many years before flight to the Moon became practicable. But we have no more than the vaguest idea of the scene near a neutron star.

The 'black hole'

The most extreme concept of all is that of a so-called 'black hole', in which the mass is so great that even the neutron-star stability is destroyed. There is an implosion (the opposite of an explosion), and the star collapses totally. It becomes a singularity in the space-time continuum, which is another way of saying that to all intents and purposes its immense gravitational field closes up space round it, and it becomes inaccessible to us; so far as we are concerned, it has left our universe, though we may still see dust as gas circling around it. Recently it has been suggested that the fainter component of the eclipsing binary Epsilon Aurigæ (close to Zeta Aurigæ in the sky) may be a black hole rather than a very large, cool star; there have even been suspicions about the fainter component of Beta Lyræ. However, our knowledge is still very limited, and the whole concept is a difficult one. Meantime we can at least study the normal novæ, which may be mild by comparison, but are fully capable of devastating their planets to leave the wild, terrifying scene shown in the painting opposite.

A destroyed planet *right*
On the very outskirts of a hypothetical planetary system – the 'Pluto' of the system, in fact, since the planet has narrowly escaped destruction when the primary star flared up as a nova, increasing its luminosity by 70,000 times and vaporizing all its inner planets. Any atmosphere or seas which this remaining planet once possessed have been blasted into space; once-tall mountains have been melted like candle-wax, and the surface is cracked and barren, scattered with glass-like globules of rock. The sky is enriched by an aurora-like display, caused by the shell of gases released by the star as its outer layers expand, fluorescing in many colours under the ultra-violet radiation. The primary is double; the red giant looks like a ghost behind the bright blue star.

The Ring Nebula in Lyra *below*
photographed from Palomar with the 48-inc Schmidt telescope. This is the best-known of the planetary nebulæ – which are neither planets nor nebulæ! Such an object consists of a faint, hot central star surrounded by a shell of gas; it is possible that this shell is the result of a nova outburst.

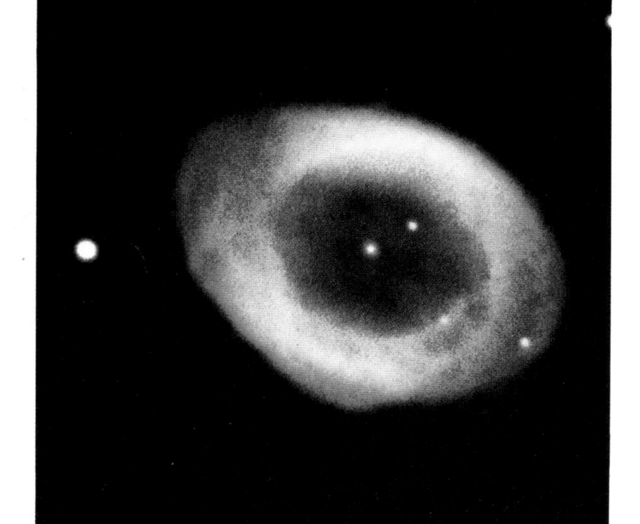

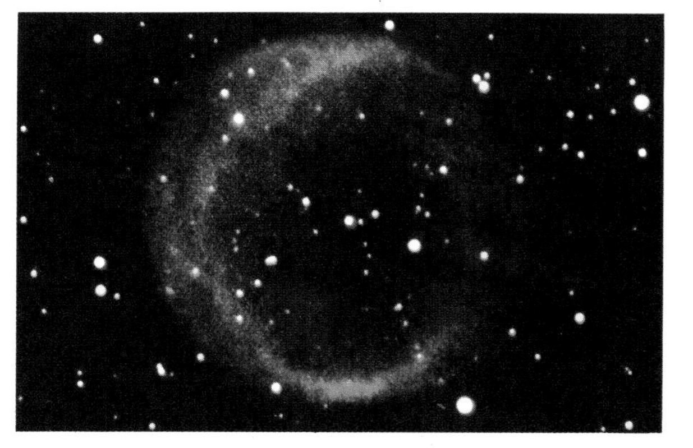

A planetary nebula *above*
NGC 6781 in Aquarius (the Water-bearer), again photographed from Palomar. Unlike the Ring, it is too faint to be seen in a small telescope, and the shell is less complete, indicating a more advanced stage in evolution. Most of the stars scattered in the photograph lie in the foreground.

DISTANT STARS 6

Nebulæ are of three types, though the apparent difference between the classes is superficial rather than actual. If the nebula contains very hot, energetic stars, the tenuous material is made to shine by its own light as well as by reflection; this produces what is called an emission nebula. The Trifid Nebula, shown above, is of this type. If the stars in the nebula are less powerful, as with the Pleiades, the nebula shines only by reflection. Finally, a nebula unlit by any intermixed stars will not shine at all; it will be a dark mass, betraying its presence only because it blots out objects beyond. Dark rifts can be seen in the Trifid, and there is a very prominent dark nebula in the Southern Cross, known appropriately, because of its shape and colour, as 'the Coal-Sack'.

From Earth, the Trifid Nebula – known officially as Messier 20, or NGC 6514 – is a faint glow in the constellation of Sagittarius. Photographs with large telescopes and long exposures are needed to show it in its full splendour. It is 30 light-years in diameter, and its distance from us is 2,300 light-years, so that we see it today as it used to be before the time of Julius Cæsar. It is gloriously coloured, and these colours can be recorded photographically, though they are too fugitive to be seen with the naked eye no matter what telescope is used. Its apparent diameter is almost equal to that of the full moon. In it are bright gaseous regions, excited by the hot stars within so that they shine by their own light; there are dark rifts, where we see the unlit material. Also we can see circular, small dark spots, known as globules and usually associated with the name of a great contemporary American astronomer, Bart J. Bok. It is thought that these globules will eventually shrink and heat up inside, so that they will turn into stars. The Trifid Nebula, then, is a stellar birthplace. Can men ever go there?

There seems no valid reason why not – assuming that interstellar travel will

eventually become possible. The nebular material is very tenuous – many millions of times less dense than our atmosphere, so that a rocket probe could pass through it as easily as through what we usually but erroneously call 'empty space'. But the best view of the Trifid would be obtained from outside it, and the painting shows the scene from a hypothetical planetary system only 60 light-years from its boundary. The planet itself is seen together with a satellite, with the incredible, glowing gas-clouds acting as a backdrop. The planet is of terrestrial type, while the rocky satellite more closely resembles our Moon. The design of a star-ship, such as the one shown here, is of course conjectured: this is assumed to be a 'photon rocket', the giant parabolic reflector emitting a beam of light particles. The light of another 'moon' behind us is reflected by the dark portions of the two worlds. The star around which the planet moves is out of the picture, to the right.

An astronomer on a planet in this position would have a fascinating view of the way in which stars are born; the process is admittedly a slow one, but when a star blows away its surrounding ring of dust and begins to shine brightly it can do so quite suddenly. No doubt this is happening all the time to the embryo stars in the Trifid. Also, the structure of the gas and dust would change over relatively short periods; there could be no thought of an unchanging sky, such as that in which our ancestors used to believe.

The Trifid is not the brightest emission nebula visible from Earth; the nebula in the Sword of Orion is more conspicuous, mainly because it is closer (1,500 light-years) – but for sheer beauty the Trifid remains unsurpassed.

Journey to the Trifid Nebula *above*
A view of a planet, with its satellite, sixty light-years from the huge emission nebula nicknamed the Trifid. The planet, shown to the right, has a terrestrial-type atmosphere, but since its axis of rotation is at almost right-angles to the plane of the orbit round its sun(out of the picture, to the right) the cloud-patterns are much more symmetrical than ours, and form parallel bands. The large satellite, higher up, is rocky; the light of another satellite coming from 'behind' causes a faint glow on the dark hemispheres of the two worlds. Its motors barely cooling, a star-ship goes into orbit in the life-zone of the planetary system. At its tip, beyond the fuel tanks, shielding and crew-spheres, are small ferry rockets for descent to the planet.

INTERSTELLAR COMMUNICATION

Communication with astronauts on the Moon is a very easy matter indeed. Neither will there be any difficulty with Mars, or indeed with any of the worlds in the Solar System. The slight delay (up to five hours or so with the outermost planets) will be no more than irritating. However, communicating with hypothetical civilizations living on planets moving round other stars is a problem of a different order. Certainly we can have no hope of sending a twentieth-century type rocket probe there; the time of travel would be hopelessly long. Even light, moving at 186,000 miles per second, takes more than four years to reach us from the nearest star. Radio waves, of course, move at the same velocity as light, and if we are to establish contact it can only be by means of radio. But apart from all other difficulties communication will be slow. Even with Proxima Centauri, a message transmitted in (say) 1972 would not arrive until 1976, and no reply would be possible before 1980 at the earliest.

All the available evidence indicates that planet families are common in the Galaxy. If this is so, then we may assume that there are also many civilizations, some of which may have achieved a far higher level of technology than we have as yet managed to do. They, too, must have their radio telescopes and their radio astronomers; what are our chances of 'tuning in' to them?

Obviously, the difficulties are very great. It is not easy even to pick up natural radio emissions from ordinary stars; in fact very few stars have so far been identified in the radio range. Early in 1972 C. M. Wade and R. M. Hjellming, at Green Bank, discovered that both Algol and Beta Lyræ are radio sources; the only other stars of the same kind are Antares B and the star associated with the X-ray source Cygnus X-1. (It may or may not be coincidental that all four are eclipsing binaries.) The other radio sources are supernova remnants, gas-clouds, galaxies and quasars. Artificial transmissions from a planet moving round another star would inevitably be feeble and hard to identify.

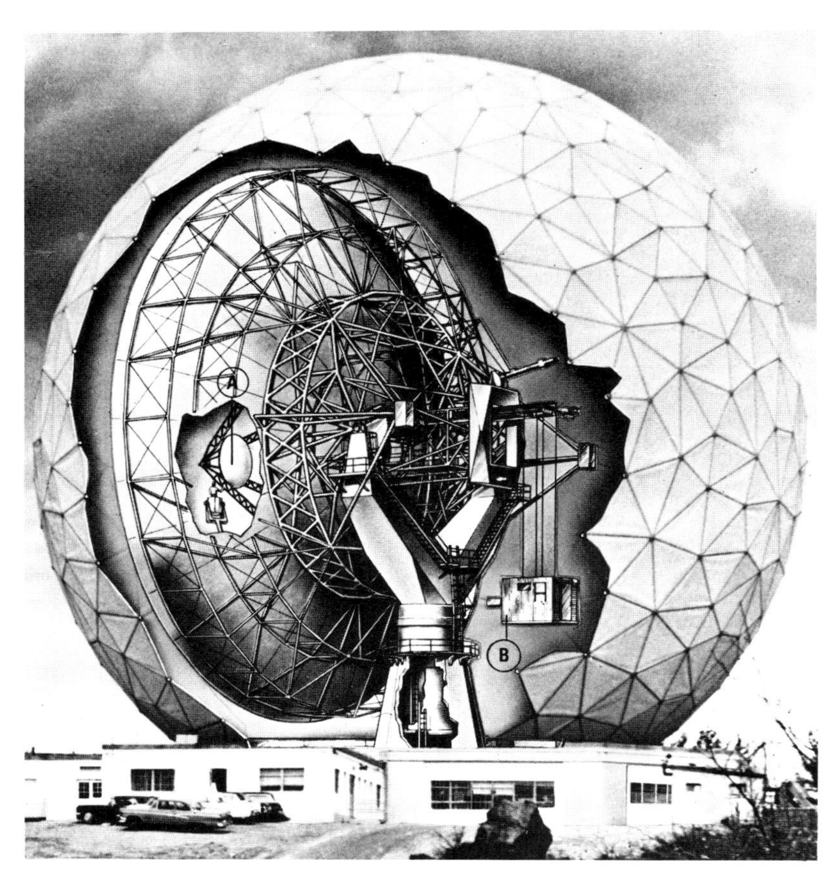

Haystack Radio Telescope *right*
The Haystack radio telescope of the Massachusetts Institute of Technology, Lincoln Laboratory. Above is a drawing showing some details of the radio telescope, which has a diameter of 120 feet. An operator is shown adjusting the 9-foot secondary reflector (A). A 2-ton special purpose electronics box (B), is hoisted into place to be plugged into the antenna. The boxes are interchangeable to permit different kinds of experiment. The covering 'radome' is 150 feet in diameter, and constructed on geodetic principles.

Project Ozma

In 1960 radio astonomers at Green Bank, West Virginia, began an ambitious programme known officially as Project Ozma. With powerful equipment, they concentrated upon the two nearest stars which are reasonably like the Sun – Tau Ceti and Epsilon Eridani, both of which are rather smaller and cooler than the Sun and are more than 10 light-years away. It was thought possible that either star might be attended by an inhabited planet, and the Ozma researchers were trying to pick up rhythmical signals which might be interpreted as artificial. They selected a wavelength of 21.2 centimetres, since this is the wavelength of the radio signals emitted by the clouds of cold hydrogen spread through the Galaxy. It was logical to believe that other radio astronomers, wherever they might be, would also be devoting their attention to this particular wavelength.

Ozma was (not unexpectedly!) negative, and was soon discontinued; but it was not unreasonable, and in the future it may be tried again. A suitable site for the equipment would be on the far side of the Moon, where the powerful transmitting stations on Earth can cause no interference with incoming signals. Admittedly the chances of success are slight; but they are not nil, and at present they represent our best hope of proving, once and for all, that other civilizations exist.

Radio contact

Conversely, it may well be that alien radio astronomers are at this moment 'listening out' in the region of the Sun. They may know nothing of the Earth, which is so small that across galactic distances it will be excessively hard to detect; but they may pick up our radio signals. If so, they will know that 'beings' of some kind exist in the Sun's system. Clearly, radio methods of contact between one planetary system and another are restricted, and information will always be out of date. If, to take an extreme example, we could pick up a rhythmical signal from a planet moving round a star 600 light-years away, all we could prove is that radio astronomers existed there 600 years ago! Perhaps, in the future, other methods such as thought-communication will be developed; but as yet we have no idea of how this might be done, so that speculation is both endless and pointless.

Horn antenna at Andover, Maine *left*
Situated inside a 'radome', one of the first major uses of this radio telescope was tracking the Telstar satellite in 1962. The size of the antenna is indicated by the man standing beneath the 'dish'.

Interstellar contact *right*
An alien radio telescope, directed upward at an alien sky. The design is much the same as that of our own Jodrell Bank paraboloid; but in the sky our hypothetical planet has a vast moon, with its sun low down over the horizon. Perhaps the scientists there are studying the region of the Sun, many light-years away; perhaps they will be successful in establishing that a peopled planet exists in the Sun's system – and perhaps, one day, they will be able to contact us.

CONCLUSION

In this book we have looked into the future. Starting with our home, the Earth, we have passed from space-stations to the Moon, the Sun's family of planets, and thence to the distant stars. Yet are we being over-speculative and unrealistic? As our rockets fly further from our home, it is an appropriate time to take stock of our situation and see what lies in store for us.

There is no need to do more than repeat that only a few decades ago the idea of travel to the Moon was ridiculed. Today transmitting stations have been set up there, and Earth-made vehicles stand on the surfaces of Venus and Mars. Interplanetary flight cannot lie very far ahead. But when we consider the stars, the problems are not hundreds but thousands or even millions of times more difficult. The distances involved are so immense that it is impossible to conceive of them in normally recognizable terms.

Are we justified in saying that the stars are forever beyond our reach? The answer can only be 'no', even though as yet we have no hard and fast ideas of how the journey can be accomplished. To us, a journey to Sirius, to Zeta Aurigæ or to the star-studded core of a globular cluster seems less fantastic than Mariner 9, or even Sputnik I, would have seemed to Sir Isaac Newton.

The illustration on the right imagines a scene at night on a planet of a star in such a cluster. Globular clusters are relatively compact systems. They belong to our galaxy, but all are very remote – over 20,000 light-years away. They form a kind of 'outer framework' to the Galaxy, and are made up of Population II stars, so that their most luminous stars are old red giants that have evolved away from the Main Sequence. They are symmetrical, and may contain upward of half a million stars equal in luminosity to the Sun, together with an uncertain but very large number of dimmer stars which we cannot see individually.

It is not easy to believe that any material vehicle could ever take an Earth-traveller as far as a globular cluster; remember that even moving at the velocity of light, a probe would take over twenty thousand years! Yet there is no reason why the stars in a cluster should not have planet-families.

Alien life forms *above*
The final painting is the most speculative of all, for it attempts to show a totally alien life-form: oxygen-filled sacs which are capable of floating freely in the winds of a carbon dioxide atmosphere. To any inhabitants with senses resembling our own, the 'night' on a planet of a star in a globular cluster would be beautiful and fascinating, with its thousands of stars – many as bright as Sirius, and others as brilliant as our full Moon.

Planet in a globular cluster
The planet shown here is assumed to have an atmosphere sufficiently thick to support life. There can be no night as we know it; the sky is filled with thousands of stars, many of which would be as brilliant as Sirius appears to us, while others would be as bright as our full Moon. The light background to the nearer stars is caused not by atmosphere, but by cloud upon cloud of more remote stars. The prevailing colour is warm and rosy, since, as we have noted, the most luminous cluster-stars are red giants. The nearest stars will be only light-months away, but even so the separations amount to thousands of millions of miles, so that stellar collisions must be extremely rare. In the picture, we see a satellite of our hypothetical planet.

The survival of civilizations
The most exciting prospect of all is the chance of contacting other intelligent races. It is logical to suppose that where life can arise, life will arise – and will evolve to the highest degree possible according to its environment. The picture in our scene is quite outside our normal experience – unless perhaps one is reminded of protoplasmic life-forms in the sea – but it is possible to build up a whole 'ecology' for a hypothetical planet. Here the artist postulated massive colonies of oxygen-filled bladders, anchored to land or forming great rafts on an ocean, maturing and finally floating free into a carbon dioxide atmosphere, where they rise and travel in atmospheric winds. Such a scene is of course pure speculation, but one of the biggest questions remaining is, 'Can life take such totally alien forms, or will it, if encountered, be basically Earthlike?'

How many civilizations will survive is another matter. Some, no doubt, will destroy themselves by warfare as soon as they have split the atom and learned enough to render their homelands uninhabitable. Others will be wiped out by natural calamities. The rest may, we are entitled to hope, progress far beyond our own present primitive state. Their needs and their ambitions may be totally different from ours, but there are certain common factors. Astronomy must be as fascinating to them as it is to us, and at this moment there may be many optical telescopes and radio telescopes pointed skyward – some, unquestionably, in the direction of the Earth.

Whether we shall be the first in the Galaxy to achieve inter-stellar travel remains to be seen, and it is not a question which can be answered in the lifetime of anyone living in the twentieth century. But so long as life on Earth survives and progresses, so Man will continue his attempts to reach out into the Universe. Apollos and Mariners will give way to deep-space probes, then to star-ships and finally, perhaps, to vehicles which can travel across the vast gulfs between the galaxies. They may not be material ships, but in the 6,000 million years remaining to us before the Sun turns into a red giant we must make our journeys beyond the Solar System. We can never ignore the supreme challenge of the stars.